Mammals
of Britain and Europe

A CONCISE GUIDE IN COLOUR

Mammals
of Britain and Europe

by Dr Jan Hanzak

Illustrated by Dagmar Cerna

HAMLYN

LONDON • NEW YORK • SYDNEY • TORONTO

Translated by Margot Schierlová

Line drawings by Vratislav Mazák
Graphic design by Soňa Valoušková

Designed and produced by Artia for
THE HAMLYN PUBLISHING GROUP LIMITED
London · New York · Sydney · Toronto
Astronaut House, Feltham, Middlesex, England

ISBN 0 600 36079 2

Printed in Czechoslovakia by Polygrafia Prague
3/02/12/51

CONTENTS

PREFACE

From the spring onwards, right into winter, we may encounter many species of mammals everywhere — in woods, fields and meadows, in the lowlands and high up in the mountains and even in the vicinity of human communities. It is true that we do not always see them as often as birds, partly because birds are more numerous and partly because many mammals are more retiring and frequently come out in search of food early in the morning or in the evening. Nevertheless, they are a very important group of animals. Many of them are of considerable economic significance, e.g. as game, as livestock, in forestry or as laboratory animals. Even so, we know all too little about them. How many people can really distinguish a hare from a rabbit, a polecat from a marten or a weasel from a stoat? Not to mention the huge tribes of voles and mice, or the tiny shrews, which are often mistaken for mice. With bats, the situation is even worse and the number of people who can identify the individual species is very small indeed. In fact, some people still regard bats as hairy relatives of birds.

Some species of mammals have been greatly reduced in numbers or actually wiped out by man, while in other cases he has helped their spread and development. A few examples of the latter process are given in this book. For instance, the musk rat is now so completely at home

7

in Europe that we no longer realize that it originally came from America.

Because of the limited size of this book, we were obliged to restrict our choice to the most interesting and more common European species of mammals. Marine species (pinnipeds and cetaceans) have been left out altogether and many species of bats also had to be omitted.

The text briefly describes the main characteristics and interesting peculiarities of the various species of mammals selected, with special emphasis on their habits and environment, based on the latest findings. We hope that our little book will encourage the reader to take a deeper interest in this class of animals in general and in species inhabiting the continent of Europe in particular.

ABOUT MAMMALS IN GENERAL

Like fishes, amphibians, reptiles and birds, mammals are vertebrates, i.e. they have an internal skeleton including a spine composed of vertebrae, which forms the longitudinal axis of their body.

Among the vertebrates, only mammals and birds maintain a constant body temperature, making them independent of climatic conditions. They are therefore described as 'warm-blooded' (homoiothermic) animals.

Mammals have a highly developed brain of complicated structure with a thick outer layer of grey matter (the cortex), which is the seat of their relatively well developed mental function.

The lower jaw articulates with the skull, thereby allowing mastication, i.e. the chewing of food in the oral cavity. Four types of teeth are differentiated — chisel-like incisors for biting off morsels of food, canines for gripping or killing prey and premolars and molars for grinding food. Mammals' dentition can be specialized in various ways; the canines or upper incisors may be absent, the canines may have a special form and several basic types

I. Mammal's dentition
teeth types

9

of molars are also differentiated. The number and shape of the teeth is always specific for a given group, however.

The mammalian heart has four compartments and the circulatory system is divided into an arterial and a venous component. The arteries carry blood away from the heart and the veins carry it back to the heart, where it receives fresh oxygen from the lungs.

As a rule, the body is covered with fur composed of separate hairs, which are an outgrowth of the skin and are a specific feature of mammals. The thick under-coat, which is the main heat-insulator, is sometimes very fine, while the longer hairs protruding above it are coarser. It is usually the long hairs which give the animal its typical appearance and colour. Some mammals are covered with scales, spines or bristles, however, and there are even species which are hairless.

Nails, claws and hooves are also a product of the keratinous (horny) layer of the skin. Hooves, which are

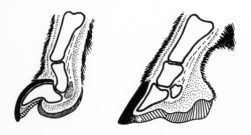

11. Diagram of nail (left) and hoof (right)

the most complex of these structures, completely cover the last joint of the toes. Other keratinous structures include horns (antlers are a bony formation), scales, plates and spines.

Only the lowest order of mammals, the monotremes, lay eggs. All other species give birth to live young. During its development in the female's body, the embryo receives its nourishment through a special organ — the placenta. After birth, the young are reared on maternal milk obtained from the mammary glands, which are a specific type of skin gland. Skin glands are another typical feature of mammals. Of their several types, the most widely distributed are the sweat glands. Scent glands, which are usually situated near the anus, but may also occur on the head, limbs and other parts of the body, have an important biological role in the life of mammals, however. The animals use the substances which they secrete to inform each other of their presence, or to mark out their domain.

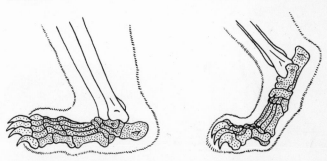

III. Diagram of hind limbs in plantigrades (left) and digitigrades (right)

Animals with well developed scent glands must obviously have a keen sense of smell. In many mammals, this is the most highly developed sense of all and it literally enables them to 'smell' danger. Most mammals have excellent vision and only forms living in the dark or underground have rudimentary eyes. Mammals likewise hear extremely well. The best developed sense naturally varies with the species and its mode of life. Cats rely primarily on their vision and deer on their sense of smell, but all of them have excellent hearing. Taste is usually mediated through specialized cells localized in the mucous membrane of the oral cavity, and by taste buds in the tongue. Tactile cells (for the sense of touch) are usually localized in the skin, the largest number being found on the palms, soles, lips, snout, etc., i.e. on those parts of the body with the greatest direct contact with the environment.

Mammals can be divided into groups according to the way in which they walk — plantigrade (on the whole of the sole) and digitigrade (on the toes only). Intermediate groups also exist (e.g. the rabbit, the marten).

The mammal class (Mammalia) comprises about four thousand species. European species inhabit every type of environment — fields, woods (deciduous and conifer), water and even the bare, inhospitable rocks of high mountains.

HOW TO OBSERVE AND STUDY MAMMALS

The observation of mammals in their natural surroundings is much more difficult than bird-watching. The main difference is that birds are more active during the daytime, can be seen more easily as they fly from place to place and are more vocal than mammals, so that they often draw attention to their presence over a considerable distance. Birds' nests are likewise often easier to find than mammals' dens and, if we exercise a little caution, birds are easier to approach. A great many mammals hunt or graze mainly in the evening and early morning, and if we want to see them, therefore, we must obviously be present at the times they are active. These can be some of the most beautiful times of day and nature further offers us the opportunity of meeting different animals as they come out to hunt or graze, or return to their hiding-place after a nocturnal stroll. Early morning walks are an essential condition if we really want to become acquainted with the fauna of a given region in detail, or learn interesting facts about its life. If we wait until eight o'clock, we shall never see a troupe of wild boars rooting in the ground, never catch a glimpse of a marten hunting squirrels, never be able to observe a fox catching mice on the outskirts of a wood. It is precisely in the early hours of the morning and on bright, moonlit nights that we can experience the most unforgettable adventures.

The success of such outings partly depends on how

lightfooted we are, the main thing being to make as little noise as possible. Soft, rubber-soled footwear is therefore recommended. Animals will take to flight before a noisy group comes anywhere near them and so such walks are best undertaken alone. Besides, when we are alone, we are more absorbed, are not distracted and are aware of the slightest movement.

Animals with a well-developed sense of smell (e.g. deer) must be approached upwind. Otherwise they will scent us a long way away and will be gone before we can even see them!

So far we have spoken only about nature walks. These are to be recommended chiefly for those who can move quietly, who know how to make use of the ground or vegetation for taking cover and who are lightfooted and react by treading softly on every twig felt under their foot. For those with little experience of this 'Red Indian' method of stalking, it will be better to try lying in wait. Here, the most important factor is patience. This method does not provide the variety of a change of scene, or the joy of coming up on one's objective unobserved, but it has other advantages. If we find a good hiding-place with a clear view, and if we can endure the long wait, the animal will often come up quite close to us, so that we can watch its activities for some time.

The best spots for watching are near game 'runs', the outskirts of grazing grounds and the vicinity of 'soiling' places and drinking pools.

The two methods, i.e. stalking and watching, can be combined. In that case, the best places for watching are look-outs in trees or on rocks, or the artificial platforms built by gamekeepers. We can make a simple platform ourselves in a suitable place in the branches of a tree. All we need to do is to lay or nail a board on a horizontal branch or the fork of two branches.

The presence and activities of mammals can be determined indirectly from the different marks which they leave behind them. These are not necessarily only paw or claw tracks in soft ground or snow. They include faeces, the remains of a meal, digging and rooting marks and scratches on the bark of trees. From these traces we can try to determine the places which the animals frequent and where they have their burrows, lairs, dens, beds and lodges. (A burrow is a hole dug in the ground, a bed is a pit in the ground, a den is a semi-hollow or hollow retreat, a lair is a lined den or bed and a lodge is the lair of a beaver or an otter.) The marks an animal leaves behind tell us what type of food it eats, while its tracks, as well as showing what species it belongs to, tell us whether it was undisturbed or running away and whether it was alone or one of the herd.

Tracks in the snow provide diverse information on the mammal population of a given region. If we follow the tracks of one animal, we learn something about its nocturnal wanderings, its prey and encounters with other animals. New snow is the best for track-reading, as the marks are fresh and not a criss-cross network of old tracks. An enthusiast never neglects such an opportunity, but after a snowfall, is out early in the morning, to see what animals there are about.

Good binoculars are an important aid for nature observations, but to start with it is better to try to manage without them. In this way we can best test our ability to come up close to animals and learn caution and circumspection.

Binoculars are today part of the naturalist's normal equipment, as they enable animals to be observed and identified from a considerable distance, without disturbing them. The most satisfactory are field-glasses giving six- to ten-fold enlargement. We should make sure that the f-number of the instrument is large enough, however, so that it always allows observation in a poor light.

Up to now we have discussed only the observation of mammals, but sometimes it is necessary to catch an animal, alive or dead. Since the body form and habits of mammals are very diverse, the ways of catching them likewise vary. The hunting and catching of large and moderately large mammals is usually subject to certain regulations.

Small mammals (voles, mice and shrews) are caught with ordinary spring traps, in automatically closing boxes and snares, or in glass drums imbedded in the ground, from which the animal cannot climb out once it has fallen in.

The traps are baited with all kinds of food, the commonest of which is bacon rind cut into small pieces. A bread-crust spread with fat and toasted over a candle-flame, or a piece of wick soaked in fat and smoked in a candle-flame can also be recommended. These universal baits are used for catching rodents and shrews.

Herbivorous species, such as voles and mice, readily fall for chopped vegetables (carrots or parsnips), while insectivores can also be tempted by plant bait, e.g. nuts. In general, any bait containing fat is suitable for both rodents and insectivores; the latter, being flesh-eaters, can further be caught with meat.

Some animals cannot be caught with bait at all, however. In that case, an ordinary spring trap can be adapted to function on contact. We can either add a wide 'treadle', or connect the spring mechanism to an obstacle, which triggers the device off when it is crossed.

A whole series of publications is available, describing a wide range of traps and snares and explaining many methods of catching animals for different purposes. They usually also describe simple methods of preparing and mounting the animals.

All nature observations should be recorded in a note-book, immediately on the spot. This is an essential condition of field work. The notes must always include the place and date of the observation, remarks on the weather and details on the animal's activities, on the observation of tracks, etc. Later on, when elaborating the results, you will see how important apparently minor details can be. In principle, notes can be kept in two ways. We can either arrange the individual observations in chronological order, i.e. as they occur, or according to animal species, in which case the relevant observations are added to the records of the species concerned. This means keeping an alphabetical list of species. We can, of course, put down our actual observations in chronological

17

order and afterwards, at home, sort them out according to species. When catching mammals, every specimen should be marked at once, on the spot, by attaching a label, supplied with a serial number, to its leg. In the definitive records it is registered under this number and its species, the place and date of the find, a description of the environment and the animal's sex and age are given. The measurements and weight of each specimen are also added.

Taking mammals' measurements is absolutely essential for further elaboration and scientific evaluation of the collection. A standard measuring method has been evolved, allowing the comparison of results obtained by different workers. The methods by which the members of the various orders are measured differ in respect of a few details only.

The following basic measurements are determined in all mammals:

1. Head and body length. The animal is placed on a flat board and its length, from the tip of its snout to the base of its tail, is measured with a ruler or with dividers.

2. Tail length. This is measured from the base to the tip, but without the terminal hairs. In mammals with a bushy tail, it can also be measured together with the terminal hairs. This length is given in brackets after the true length.

IV. *Method of measurement of mammals* 1 — head and body length 2 — tail length 3 — hind paw length 4 — ear length 5 — height at the shoulder 6 — tragus length 7 — forearm length 8 — condylobasal length of skull 9 — width of skull

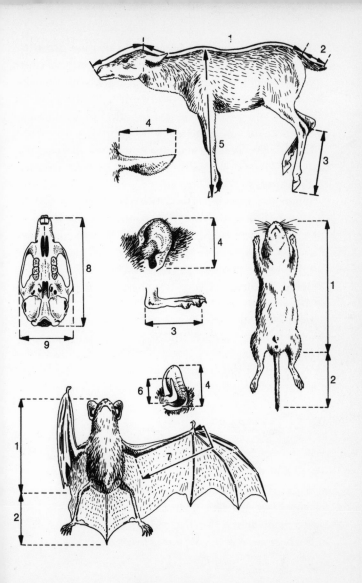

3. Hind paw length. Measured from the heel to the tip of the longest digit, minus the claw.

4. Ear length. Measured from the notch at the base to the tip, again minus the terminal tuft of hairs. In large mammals, other measurements can also be determined, as given in the appended drawings.

In bats, the forearm length is one of the determining features. The method by which it is measured is shown in the drawing.

Where we encounter the expression 'skull length' in the description of the mammals in this book, it refers to the condylobasal length of the skull. This is the length measured from the anterior margin of the upper jaw to the hindmost process of the occipital tubercle (the occipital condyle), where the first cervical vertebra articulates with the skull.

Another important factor in the identification of mammals is the number and size of the teeth and the length of the row.

INSECTIVORES
(Insectivora)

All European species of mammals belong to the higher, or placental mammals — so called because a placenta is formed in the female's body during embryogenesis, providing nourishment for the embryo. Mammals evolved at the beginning of the Mesozoic Era from certain groups

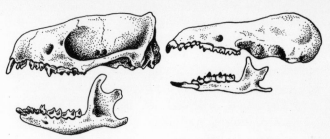

V. Hedgehog's skull

VI. Insectivore's skull
(shrew of the *Sorex* genus)

of reptiles and their oldest representatives most closely resembled insectivores.

Insectivores are the most primitive placental mammals, as seen from a number of features of their body structure. They have a small, simple brain and phylogenetically primitive dentition with a large number of teeth (28 to 44), of which the molars are very similar to those of the oldest extinct mammals. When walking, they tread on the whole of their sole — another sign of a low degree of development. They are small animals and actually include the smallest mammal in existence — Savi's pygmy shrew, which weighs only 2 grammes and lives in the Mediterranean region and in central and southern Asia. The largest members of the order are about the size of a cat. Practically all of them have five digits, an elongate skull, on which the zygomatic arches are often absent, and a particularly long nose, which tapers off in a mobile snout. The snout is controlled by muscles allowing it, in some species, to be turned up, so that it looks like a tiny trunk. Since insectivores are guided mainly by their sense of smell and, in addition, have long tactile hairs on the tip of their nose, their snout is never at rest.

The insectivores are a numerous group of mammals, but because they are not, on the whole, very conspicuous, our knowledge of them is still incomplete and we do not even know how many species there are. They occur everywhere except Australia, a large part of South America and the polar regions. They are adapted for life on the ground, underground and in the water and some species can actually climb trees. This adaptation to different types of environment has naturally resulted in different forms of specialization in body structure. To take an example close at hand, the mole, with its shovel-like fore limbs, cylindrical body and other features, is perfectly equipped for a subterranean existence. The hedgehog is protected from danger by a coat of spines, the movements of which are controlled by a special subcutaneous muscle, while among non-European insectivores we find some with long hind legs on which they jump like little kangaroos.

As indicated by their name, insectivores live mainly on insects. They are not solely dependent on insects for sustenance, however, but devour all kinds of invertebrates and even small vertebrates. The amount of vegetable food they eat is restricted. They cannot tolerate long fasts and consume large amounts of food. Their sensitivity to food shortages is evidently the reason why some insectivores, such as the hedgehog, hibernate. During hibernation, the function of all their organs is largely depressed. For example, the hedgehog's body temperature can fall from a normal $+33°C$ to $+1.5°C$. Similarly, its heart rate falls from 188 to 21 beats a minute. The hedgehog does not hibernate in a warm nest, but sometimes simply under a layer of fallen leaves, and if the environmental temperature rises, it wakes up.

Although the shrews (family Soricidae) are the most numerous group of insectivores, we know little about them. One sign of our ignorance is that they are often mistaken for mice. They are tiny, but extremely active animals and are always looking for prey. All of them are sensitive to their environmental conditions and if these are inclement they soon die. Their life is very short and they seldom survive a second winter.

Shrews are often eaten by birds of prey and owls. Beasts of prey, on the other hand, frequently catch them, but then cast them aside, evidently repelled by their pungent, musky odour.

This important group of very useful animals merits more attention than it has hitherto received.

BATS
(Chiroptera)

Bats include both carnivorous species and the fruit-eating bats of the tropics. They are not, as a rule, very large, but the biggest has a wing span of about 150 cm. European bats are all small.

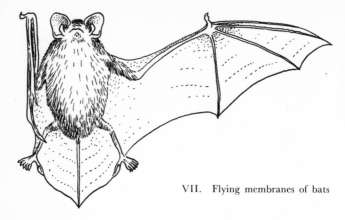

VII. Flying membranes of bats

Among mammals we find many species capable of travelling through the air. These animals have flaps of skin on their sides, which permit gliding, i.e. passive flight. The only mammals capable of active flight are bats. They have a fluttering type of flight and do not move very fast, but they can rise and fall, describe curves and suddenly veer, so that they are able to catch insects while flying. As with birds, their organ of flight is the

VIII. *Ear shapes of some European bats*
1 – Brown bat *(Myotis myotis)* 2 – *Myotis oxygnathus* 3 – Geoffroy's bat *(Myotis emarginatus)* 4 – Bechstein's bat *(Myotis bechsteinii)* 5 – Natterer's bat *(Myotis nattereri)* 6 – Whiskered bat *(Myotis mystacinus)* 7 – Water bat *(Myotis daubentoni)* 8 – Pond bat *(Myotis dasycneme)* 9 – Noctule bat *(Nyctalus noctula)* 10 – Leisler's bat *(Nyctalus leisleri)* 11 – Common bat *(Pipistrellus pipistrellus)* 12 – Nathusius' pipistrelle *(Pipistrellus nathusii)* 13 – Particoloured bat *(Vespertilio discolor)* 14 – Northern bat *(Eptesicus nilssoni)* 15 – Serotine *(Eptesicus serotinus)* 16 – Barbastelle *(Barbastella barbastellus)*

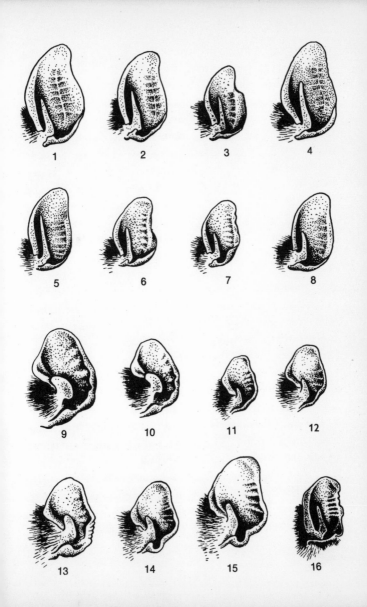

modified fore limb, on which the forearm and all the digits, except the thumb, are extremely long. A thin, sensitive skin, known as the patagial membrane, covered with a few, sparse hairs, is stretched between their fingers, body and hind limbs. This membrane has the same function as a bird's wing. Both the fore and hind limbs have the full number of digits, but the only free digits on the fore limbs are the thumbs, which terminate in claws, used by the bat for climbing and creeping. The digits on the hind limbs are mostly free, relatively small and equipped with claws. It is hard to imagine that they could be used for any purpose other than awkward, rather ungainly climbing. Another peculiarity of bats is the spur-like bone which projects from their heel and has the function of stretching the caudal patagial membrane between the hind limbs and the tail. When not flying, bats rest and sleep upside down, i.e. hanging head downwards — an unusual phenomenon in mammals.

Bats have membranous ears of the most diverse shapes, with a membranous valve at the base. The form of the valve and the shape of the ears are species specific and help in the identification of individual species.

The bat's flattened body (but not its wings) is covered with thick, fine fur. The individual hairs have a curious segmented, slightly branched or spiral structure, which has no parallel in any other mammals.

Bats have similar dentition to insectivores, but their incisors are poorly developed. The teeth are sharp and their number varies from 28 to 38, according to the species.

The most important sense of bats is hearing, which has the additional function of an organ of orientation. Their weak vision plays a subsidiary role in orientation. Bats cannot differentiate colours, but can distinguish light and dark shades. Since the males secrete a specific odour at pairing time, it can be assumed that olfaction is also developed in bats. Specific perception of temperature helps them to choose the most suitable places for their winter roosts. When looking for underground shelters, bats are particularly sensitive to air currents and can find well disguised and hidden openings by means of the draughts blowing out from them.

Most bats' staple diet is insects, which they catch on the wing. The tropical fruit bats live on fruit, while some of the ill-famed vampire bats of South America bite large animals and lick their blood as it flows from the wound. Species which live on the nectar of flowers are also known. In the tropics, these species help to fertilize the plants they visit, by transferring pollen.

Our European bats are extremely useful insect-killers, which do their hunting after dusk and during the night.

Apart from a few exceptions, bats are active in the evening and at night. During the daytime they sleep in the most diverse shelters, e.g. hollow trees, crevices, empty houses, caves and cellars, and do not emerge until after sundown. Tropical bats spend the day hanging from a branch of a leafy tree.

There are many such nocturnal and semi-nocturnal animals. To be able to find their way about, they have very sensitive eyes, capable of seeing in the faintest light. Even these creatures cannot see in absolute darkness, however. We know that bats have very small and imperfect eyes, but that even in absolute darkness they do not bump into obstacles. How do they find their way about under such conditions? In about 1942 it was discovered that bats, while flying at night, found their way by means of echo sounding. In addition to normal, audible sounds, they also emit sounds of ultrasonic frequency, inaudible to the human ear, which they can perceive as echoes. When flying by night, they produce these sounds at short intervals and their ear catches the echo as the sound waves rebound from obstacles. Bats thus 'hear' every obstacle and can tell its distance from the latent period of the echo. It was found that horseshoe bats emitted orientative sounds through their nose and controlled their direction by means of their seemingly grotesque facial appendages. Horseshoe bats can 'hear' obstacles at distance of up to 8 metres, while for some other bats the limit is only 1 metre.

During recent times it was discovered — mainly by attaching rings to the animals' forearm — that bats, in our latitudes, do not always stay in the same region, but that they regularly 'migrate' from their winter to their summer haunts and back again. Like birds, bats with short, wide wings usually travel shorter distances than those with long, narrow wings. They are seldom known to cover really long distances, but a common bat caught and marked near Dnepropetrovsk in the USSR was caught again, 70 days later, in southern Bulgaria, some 1,150 kilometres away, while a noctule bat actually travelled 2,500 kilometres. The ringing technique has furnished a great deal of interesting information on the biology of these mammals, but there is much which still needs explaining, so if you should come across a bat with an aluminium ring on its forearm, carefully copy the inscription on the ring and report your find, giving the place and data, to the nearest marking centre.

The reason why bats migrate is not a shortage of food, but the need to find a suitable winter shelter. Our bats hibernate, the majority spending the winter in cleft rocks,

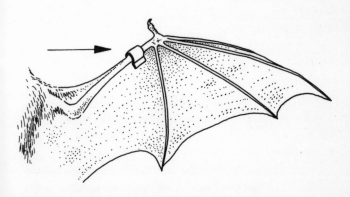

X. Attaching of ring to the bat's forearm

caves, disused barns and cellars. They sleep hanging head downwards, either singly or in groups. As in the case of other genuine hibernators (e.g. the dormouse or the hedgehog), the function of their organs falls to such a low level that the organism is kept just at the safety limit between life and death. In the waking state, their respiration rate is about 200 per minute, while during hibernation it is only 25—30 per minute, and only for about three minutes, after which there is always a pause lasting 3—8 minutes.

The only food reserves of hibernating bats is body fat deposited during the summer. Experiments showed that the body temperature of sleeping bats could be reduced to $-4°C$ without fatal results. Under natural conditions, some sort of a safety mechanism exists. If the body temperature of hibernating bats falls to a given, critical level, the animals wake and look for another, more satisfactory shelter.

The stimulus which prompts bats to start hibernating is a drop in the environmental temperature. They do not usually hibernate in places where the temperature falls below freezing point.

Under inclement environmental conditions, bats can fall into a state resembling hibernation at any time of the year, thereby saving energy. It was found that bats do not age as quickly as animals with regular activity. This is, perhaps, one of the reasons why bats, compared with other mammals of the same size, live to a comparatively old age. For instance, mice, voles and shrews seldom live through two winters and have a mean life span of a year and a half, while bats have been known to survive twelve, and even twenty, years.

The reproductive capacity of bats corresponds to their longevity. They do not need to replenish their population by producing large litters several times a year, like rodents. The female bat gives birth to only one (in some species two) young a year, whereas the litters of a female common vole total about forty. In normal circumstances, the bat population would be maintained without any danger of its diminishing, despite the small number of young, as bats have few natural enemies. Man often interferes destructively with their natural environment, however. Our cave-dwelling bats are all too often disturbed, the entrances to their underground spaces are frequently walled up and old, hollow trees are cut down. It is therefore no wonder that the number of these useful animals is rapidly decreasing.

Bats living in the temperate belt mate during the late summer and the autumn, but the eggs (ova) in the female's body are not fertilized until the spring. When giving birth, the female lies in a horizontal position, gripping the wall with its clawed thumbs as well as with its hind limbs. It then bends its tail over its abdomen to form a kind of pocket, into which the newborn young is neatly dropped. The young bat instinctively feels its way towards a teat and starts sucking. The young are born blind and hairless and their wings are still small and undeveloped. They are reared literally on the female's breast, and even after they are able to fly they occasionally return for an extra drink of milk.

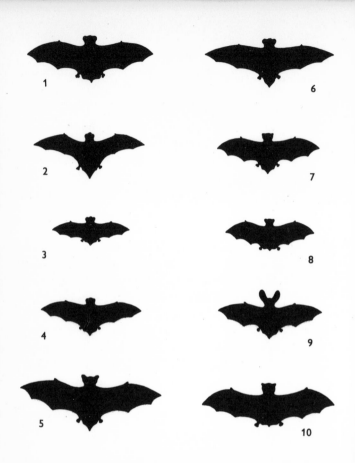

XI. *Silhouettes of some European bats*
1 — Serotine *(Eptesicus serotinus)*   2 — Long-winged bat *(Miniopterus schreibersi)*   3 — Common bat *(Pipistrellus pipistrellus)*   4 — Barbastelle *(Barbastella barbastellus)*   5 — Brown bat *(Myotis myotis)*   6 — Noctule bat *(Nyctalus noctula)*   7 — Natterer's bat *(Myotis nattereri)*   8 — Lesser horseshoe bat *(Rhinolophus hipposideros)*   9 — Long-eared bat *(Plecotus auritus)*   10 — Greater horseshoe bat *(Rhinolophus ferrumequinum)*

The total number of known species of bats is about 1,000. The majority live in tropical and subtropical regions, but there are still plenty in the temperate belt and some species occur high up in the mountains. There are no bats in the Antarctic and Arctic regions.

HARES AND RABBITS
(Lagomorpha)

Hares and rabbits have many points in common with rodents and were formerly included in the rodent order. The likeness was found to be deceptive, however, because if we study the evolution of lagomorphs and rodents, we find that they already differed in the early Tertiary Era and that they probably developed from different ancestors.

Hares and rabbits have two pairs of incisors in their upper jaw (a pair of small, narrow incisors behind the main ones), while rodents have only one pair.

XII. Difference between incisors in lagomorphs and rodents

33

The incisors are constantly worn down from in front by gnawing, have no roots and grow continuously. When biting their food, lagomorphs move their lower jaw from side to side, and not backwards and forwards as rodents do. This type of movement is made possible by special construction of the mandibular joint. The incisors and molars are separated by an empty space known as a diastema. Rodents also have a diastema, but if we compare the two groups, we find a number of distinctive differences. In lagomorphs, the distance between the teeth-rows in the upper jaw (i.e. the width of the palate) is greater than between those in the lower jaw, while in rodents the reverse is the case.

Lagomorphs also have a thickly furrowed palate, whereas in rodents there are few furrows. Lagomorphs have peculiar hairs, which are square in section, growing on their soles, but no such hairs have been found in rodents. In addition to these morphological differences, there are certain differences in behaviour. None of the lagomorphs (which include the tiny pikas, or piping hares) is able to seize its food in its fore paws, although this is quite normal among rodents. A common feature of lagomorphs is their relatively long ears, which always protrude beyond the fur and in some species (hare, rabbit) are exceptionally long. Lagomorphs' hind limbs are always somewhat longer than their fore limbs, especially in the case of hares and rabbits. The alimentary tract of lagomorphs also differs in some respects from that of rodents. For instance, they have a long, twisted appendix, in which cellulose is broken down. Being

XIII. Phases of hare's running

vegetarians, lagomorphs consume large amounts of green-stuffs, which are not very substantial and are hard to digest. Ungulates living on the same type of diet utilize their food much more completely by regurgitating it at given intervals into their mouth and re-chewing it. Lagomorphs have a different way of getting the most out of their food. They have two types of faeces. One type, the familiar round, dry pellets, is the final product of the digestive process. The other type is soft and the animal removes it from the anus with its tongue, chews it and swallows it again. It was recently demonstrated that, with the aid of intestinal bacteria, vitamin B_1 is synthesized in the appendix and that the substances secreted by the appendix contain this vitamin in an amount five times greater than in the normal faeces. In this way, therefore, lagomorphs satisfy their need for an important vitamin. The above habit has so far been determined among hares and rabbits and we do not know whether it also exists in the other family of the order, i.e. the pikas. We likewise do not know whether another phenomenon frequently demonstrated in hares is characteristic of the whole order. This is superfoetation, a state in which embryos of two different ages are present in the uterus. It means that the female can be fertilized again while already pregnant and that the litters follow each other in rapid succession.

Lagomorphs are distributed all over the world. They are not natives of Australia and New Zealand, however, but were brought there by man. The rabbit in particular became the scourge of the Australian continent. Since it had virtually no natural enemies there, and found plenty of food, it proliferated to such a degree that various drastic extermination methods had to be used to combat it, such as the artificial induction of severe infections.

All the members of the hare and rabbit family are popular with hunters and because of this they are often forgiven the appreciable damage they do to crops and by gnawing the bark of trees.

The best developed senses of lagomorphs are hearing and vision. Their auditory perception is enhanced by their relatively large ears, which they can twitch in the direction of sounds. Pikas do not possess this gift, however. These mammals, which are sometimes also known as 'mouse hares', look more like large voles, but have a very short tail.

RODENTS
(Rodentia)

Rodents are the largest order of mammals. They not only comprise about one third of all the known species of mammals, but in actual numbers they are also by far the biggest group. From time to time, many species over-proliferate until they overrun immense areas, riddle the soil with their innumerable tunnels and destroy all the vegetation within reach of their gnawing teeth. As an example, in the days when the Wild West of the USA was still one immense prairie, it was estimated that an area of 65,000 square kilometres was inhabited by some 100,000,000 prairie dogs (rodents slightly smaller than our marmot). Other examples can be found nearer home, such as the years when the fields swarm with voles.

The huge number of species and forms of rodents and their vast numbers in general are a sign that the order as a whole is today at the peak of its development. It is an order without any giants. The largest rodent, the capybara of South America, weighs 50 kilograms, but the majority of species are no larger than a mouse. Highly specialized species are also found among rodents. Some have a fold of skin on their sides, attached to their limbs, enabling them to glide through the air. Others are adapted for an aquatic, subterranean or arboreal mode of life, while others again have long hind legs permitting them to jump long distances in flat country. In a few species the body is covered with long spines. By far the greatest number of rodents are terrestrial animals.

Despite the diversity of their form, we can reliably recognize rodents from their skull. Their dentition is specifically modified for gnawing and the number of teeth varies from 12 to 22, according to the family and genus. They have no canines and in each jaw they have one pair of recurved, transformed incisors (rodent teeth). The anterior edge of these teeth is as sharp as a chisel and

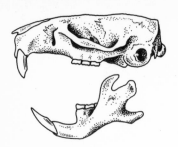

even hard material such as nutshells is unable to withstand them.

Why are the rodent teeth so sharp? Only their anterior surface is covered with enamel, while behind, their structure is much softer. This part is worn down more quickly by gnawing, thereby giving rise to a sharp, bevelled edge. The enamel is usually orange or reddish in colour and rodents use its appearance to scare enemies away. Even when the animal is resting, the rodent teeth are still clearly visible behind the cleft upper lip. When brought into actual use for defence, they can inflict deep wounds.

The rodent teeth have yet another peculiar property. Since they are constantly being ground down, they must be equally capable of continuous growth. They are very long and extend deep into the jaw, as we can see for ourselves if we extract one from the lower jaw.

Between the incisors and the molars there is a wide space known as a diastema. The molars have a very variable surface, which may be flat, cusped or ridged. When the food is being ground, the lower jaw moves backwards and forwards and not from side to side as for example in ungulates. Rodents' molars do not necessarily always have roots. In some forms, the molars do not acquire roots until the animal is quite old, while in others they never have roots.

Rodents live chiefly on plants, which, as we know, are not easily digested. Consequently, like all herbivorous animals, they have a long intestine (5—15 times longer than their body). Their appendix is also highly developed. Some rodents eat both plants and flesh. They are not fussy animals and sometimes a small patch of vegetation is sufficient for their modest requirements. They occur practically everywhere — in forests, steppes, and even deserts, near water and in rocky mountains, from the tundra to the tropical jungles. They are also natives of Australia, the home of the primitive monotremes and marsupials, where, together with a few bats, they are the only representatives of the higher, placental mammals.

Rodents are usually regarded as gregarious animals, because they mostly live in colonies. In years of over-proliferation their populations are particularly huge. Some rodents prefer to lead a solitary existence, however. One of these is the hamster. The squirrel is an inter-mediate type, as it occurs singly, but sometimes forms

XV. Various types of grinding molar surfaces in rodents
a — field mouse
b — hamster c — water vole

quite large communities, especially in places where food is abundant. The food situation is evidently also one of the causes of the mass migration of lemmings in the Scandinavian countries, where hordes of these animals periodically set out on a great exodus and die in vast numbers while trying to swim across rivers, in the sea or as a result of a long spell of bad weather.

Large species of rodents, which have fewer enemies and a longer life span, give birth to their young only once a year. Small species are exceedingly prolific and reproduce extremely quickly, producing several large litters in the course of a year. It is by no means unusual for there to be more than 10 young in one litter. The young are born blind and hairless, but make very rapid progress.

Increasing attention has been paid to the biology of rodent reproduction in recent years. Because of the damage these animals do in agriculture, man is very interested in finding new ways and means of combating them. Many questions relating to their reproduction are still unanswered. For example, we do not know the real reason why rodents over-proliferate from time to time. Nevertheless, we have learnt many interesting details, especially in the case of the common vole.

The female vole gives birth to 1—13 young at a time, according to circumstances. It can be fertilized again immediately afterwards and thus, during the reproductive season, may have a family every three weeks. The females attain sexual maturity at a very early age and can actually be fertilized before they are weaned. The reproductive season is determined by the weather, but in favourable years it can last from February until October. Reproduction may even take place during the winter. If over-proliferation occurs, voles lose their feeling for their 'preserve', i.e. the small area which they inhabit and defend. This instinct is suppressed to such a degree that several females may have young in one nest. In this situation, great rivalry develops between the males, young and weak males are excluded from reproduction by natural selection and the number of females increases. The only factors which prevent the Earth from being overrun by small rodents are their short life span (about eighteen months) and the fact that many of them die during the winter and inclement weather and that, in years of over-proliferation, the whole population dies out spontaneously within a short time from internal causes.

Apart from the damage they do to crops, forests and stocks of food, rodents are dangerous from the aspect of hygiene and health. Some of them can transmit serious diseases to man. Not all of them are pests, however, and some of them are actually useful for their flesh or their fur.

BEASTS OF PREY
(Carnivora)

Numerically, the beasts of prey are a large order of mammals. Their several families are rather dissimilar, but they possess in common various properties associated with their form of nutrition.

In general, it is right to assume that beasts of prey are

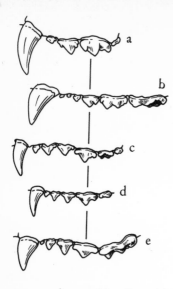

XVI. Shapes of dentition
in beasts of prey
a — cat b — bear
c — wolf d — marten
e — badger

mammals capable of catching their prey alive and then killing it. The ability of different species to do this varies. Some astound us by their dexterity or rapacity, while others are content with offal, or even occasionally turn vegetarian.

Beasts of prey have 28—42 teeth. The fox and the wolf have 42, the badger and the marten 38, the otter 36, the weasel and the polecat 34 and the wild cat and the lynx 30. The longest teeth are the canines, whose function is to seize and kill prey. The last premolar in the upper jaw and the first molar in the lower jaw have undergone transformation. They have a sharp-edged crown like a knife and are used for pulling prey to pieces. In certain omnivorous beasts of prey they are less specialized. The

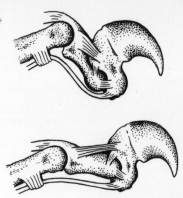

articulation of the lower jaw with the skull allows the jaw to be moved up and down only, and not in other directions like the jaw of ungulates or rodents.

The skull is surmounted by a bony crest (the sagittal crest), which is usually larger in the males than in the females. In old individuals it is large, in young ones barely discernible. It is here that the powerful masseter muscles (the muscles of mastication) are attached.

Carnivores catch their prey in different ways. Swift-footed animals hunt it down (the wolf), prowlers lie low and attack it from ambush (cats), the weasel and the eastern polecat pursue rodents right into their burrows, the badger gathers and digs for its food, martens hunt their prey on rocks and in trees and the otter is skilled at catching fish under water.

The five- or four-toed limbs are adapted accordingly, but only cats are able to catch their prey with their claws, or use their claws as a weapon. Cats' claws are curved,

43

sharp and retractile, i.e. they can be withdrawn. This prevents them from becoming blunted.

Apart from a few exceptions, beasts of prey have highly developed senses, the keenest being smell and hearing. The somewhat poor hearing of cats is compensated by their excellent vision. Scent glands, usually situated below the base of the tail, have a wide range of meanings and uses in the life of beasts of prey, which are guided chiefly by their sense of smell. The animals use the pungent substances secreted by these glands to inform others of their presence and to mark out their preserves. In the case of mustelids, the glands have become an effective defence weapon. If the animal is alarmed, it releases the secretion in such large amounts that many a would-be attacker is driven away by the offensive smell.

Beasts of prey can be claimed to possess a relatively high degree of intelligence and to have a very rich instinctive life. Their faculty for remembering and learning can be tested best in animals living in captivity.

Most beasts of prey lead a solitary existence. Of our own species, only the wolf forms small communities (packs), since it finds it more profitable to hunt in numbers, especially in the winter.

Newborn beasts of prey are blind and their auditory tubes are closed. For a long time they are helpless and completely dependent on their mother. Their infancy is spent in burrows, various types of dens or a simple lair. Some beasts of prey are monogamous, but usually only for the duration of one mating season. The males sometimes help to rear the young, but in other cases they

44

ignore their family, or may even have to be driven away by the female in case they devour their own offspring. This means that the whole task of bringing up the young falls on the female.

Beasts of prey attain sexual maturity in 1—5 years, small species maturing sooner than large ones.

The only part of the world without any native beasts of prey is Australia. The dingo (the wild dog of Australia) is the descendant of domestic dogs brought to Australia centuries ago.

Owing to their relatively well developed mental faculties, most beasts of prey can adapt themselves to different types of environments. For example, we find foxes and wolves in the tundras of the far north, in the taiga belt, in semi-desert regions and in high mountains. Geographical and ecological (i.e. environmental) factors have resulted in the development of different varieties, however, distinguishable mainly by their size and colouring. In higher latitudes, some species hibernate. Perhaps it would be more correct to say that they spend the worst time of year sleeping in their lair. They do not hibernate in the true meaning of the term, like certain rodents, insectivores and bats, since their body temperature does not fall (or only very little). During the winter some, like the badger and the bear, may wake up several times and even go outside their dens.

It was once generally held that all beasts of prey were a scourge and that they ought to be killed on sight. We now know that they have their rightful place in natural communities and that many of them are extremely useful.

Old views die hard, however, and even the killing of rare species in danger of complete extinction still goes on, despite all the laws against it. Beasts of prey play an important role in the maintenance of biological balance, e.g. by preventing over-proliferation of the rodent population. In years when their main prey over-proliferates, small beasts of prey actually reproduce at a higher rate than usual. They thus give man natural support in his fight against pests. It can be assumed that the size of the population of large carnivores, e.g. the lynx, likewise depends on the available number of the animals on which they live and is thus subject to periodic changes.

Many beasts of prey are highly valued for their fur. The fur trade is largely dependent on the number of beasts of prey, but at the same time it gravely endangers their populations.

EVEN-TOED UNGULATES
(Artiodactyla)

When describing the characteristics of even-toed ungulates, we ought to make at least a general comparison with the other ungulate order, the odd-toed ungulates (Perissodactyla), which is not represented in this book, but of which the domestic horse and domestic ass are familiar examples.

The chief feature which both the above orders have in common are hooves, which are actually transformed claws. The horny hoof completely covers the widened terminal joint of the toes, affording them very necessary protection, since these slim-legged animals walk on their toes.

Ungulates are herbivorous and cannot rely on their teeth as a weapon. Instead of fighting, they usually run away from danger. During evolution, their limbs, which are of the cursorial type, became increasingly specialized for running. Both extinct and extant forms of ungulates show that the fastest runners are those in which maximum reduction of the digits occurred during their development. As their vernacular name tells us, in odd-toed ungulates the weight of the body is carried by a single hoofed digit, while in even-toed ungulates the body is supported by two digits. The axis of their leg runs between the third and the fourth digit, which are the same size and shape and correspond to the second and third finger of the human hand. The other digits are either rudimentary or absent. There is usually a second and a fifth digit, but the animal does not walk on them, as they have shifted up the foot and do not touch the ground at all. The hippopotamus, which has four digits all the same size, is an exception.

Most even-toed ungulates are ruminants — herbivorous animals which consume large amounts of greenstuff and process their food twice. First of all they take a large meal and after a given time they chew it again ('chewing the cud'). The second phase does not require any outer activity and takes place while the animal rests. A ruminant's stomach has several parts (usually four). The first,

47

the rumen (paunch), is a kind of receptacle where the food is softened, but is not digested. From there, the food passes into the reticulum (honeycomb) from which, while the animal rests, morsels are regurgitated into the mouth and are thoroughly chewed a second time. The food then passes down a special groove in the oesophagus into the third compartment, the psalterium (manyplies). The last part, the abomasum (reed), is the true gastric organ and contains ferments. Since plant foods are digested slowly, and mainly in the intestine, all even-toed ungulates have a very long intestine. Large numbers of bacteria colonizing the gastrointestinal tract participate in the digestion of cellulose (the chief carbohydrate constituent of plants).

Non-ruminants, which include the wild boar, have a simple stomach.

Non-ruminants also have different dentition from ruminants. For example, pigs do not eat only greenstuffs, but any kind of edible material. They are therefore described as omnivorous. They possess all four types of teeth and their dentition displays no specialization for a given type of food. The molars are wide and cusped and are more like a bear's teeth than those of a herbivorous animal. Only the shape and position of the canines is typical for pigs, as they are curved and project from the gum, especially in the males. Ruminants' dentition, on the other hand, displays unilateral development for chewing vegetation. The upper incisors are absent and in their place there is a flat, cartilaginous plate. When grazing, the animal presses grass against this plate with its lower incisors and tears it off with a twitch of its head. The upper canines have either disappeared completely, or have degenerated and do not function, while the lower canines are grouped together with the incisors and have the same form. By contrast, the premolars and molars are powerfully developed, have sharp ridges and are excellently adapted for grinding. The number of teeth is very variable (28 to 44), but is always specific for the species.

In even-toed ungulates, sexual dimorphism (the existence of two distinct forms) is manifested primarily in size, the males usually being more powerfully built than the females. The males of most ruminants can also generally be identified by specific structures on their skull — antlers in deer and horns in hollow-horned ruminants. The two formations are very different, both with regard to their development and their intrinsic structure. Antlers are not a permanent, i.e. lifelong, fixture, but are shed at a given time of year and grow again. The new antler grows from a pedicle — an outgrowth of the frontal bone. After the old antler has been shed, osseous connective tissue on the surface of the pedicle begins to proliferate and the antler slowly starts growing. The new antler is covered with a fine skin, richly supplied with nerves and blood vessels for the transport of nutrients. In hunting terms, this skin is known as 'velvet'. As soon as the antler has stopped growing and has ossified, the supply of nutrients ceases and the 'velvet' begins to dry up. The deer gets rid of the old skin by rubbing its head on trees and bushes. Thus burnished, the mature antler is actually bare bone. As a rule, the antlers mature before the rutting (mating) season starts, because they are then a mark of the size and strength of the males, which employ them in duels fought for females. It would not be right to say that antlers are weapons, however, as this aspect of their

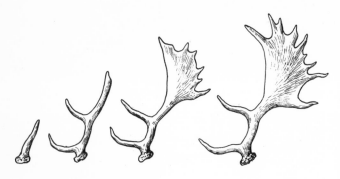

XVIII. Antler development in fallow deer (1, 3, 5 and 9 years)

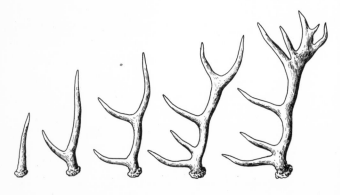

XIX. Antler development in red deer (simple antlers, pronged antlers, antlers with three, five and eight tines)

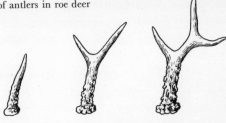

use is of secondary importance only. Their main function is to impress and intimidate. Some deer have simple antlers, while others have branched antlers forming rich 'crowns', or palmated antlers (e.g. the elk and fallow deer). Richly branched antlers do not grow all at once, however. In its second year, a red deer has only one beam, while in the following year its antlers may be branched, or may each have two to four branches (tines). The development of the antlers depends largely on heredity and on the food availability in the given area. In unfavourable circumstances they may never acquire more than two tines, or even one, but a thriving red deer (a 'royal') may have five or even more tines on each antler. We can see from these examples that the age of a male deer cannot be estimated from the number of its tines, as is often thought to be the case. A comparatively young deer may have a larger number of tines, while an old individual which is 'going back' loses its tines and may finally possess only two long beams. A deer's age can be estimated better from the signs of wear of its teeth, or from the shape of the pedicles, which grow shorter and wider with advancing age. The age of the roe deer, which seldom acquires more than four tines, likewise cannot be determined from the number of points. The fallow deer's antlers develop rather more quickly and its second antlers may already be fully palmated.

Unlike antlers, horns are permanent structures and are not shed and changed every year. They have two main parts — a bony outgrowth of the frontal bone, covered with a horny sheath formed from keratinized skin. An antler is thus a bony formation, while a horn is a transformed skin formation. If we compare the two, we might say that the bony inner stump of the horn is analogous to the pedicle of the antler, while the horny sheath is similar to the 'velvet', but converted to a hard layer which is never rubbed off. With one exception (the prong-buck of America), horns are never branched. Small horns are sometimes worn also by the females, but except for the reindeer, the female of which has simple antlers, antlers are the sole prerogative of the males.

Horns are seldom straight and are usually curved or twisted. Their growth is controlled by various factors and depends mainly on the diet and on the animal's degree of maturity. The rings, i.e. circular bulges and depressions, formed on horns can be compared to the annual growth rings of trees, as we can roughly tell the animal's age from them. Another fundamental difference between horns and antlers is that the former grow at the base and the latter at the tip.

The young of even-toed ungulates are very well developed at birth. They find their feet immediately and are able to trot beside their mother in a few hours. They are often differently coloured from their parents and sometimes they are striped, sometimes spotted. The mammary gland takes the form of an udder, which is situated between the female's hind legs and has 2—4 teats. Pigs are an exception to this rule.

The only part of the world not inhabited by even-toed ungulates is Australia and New Zealand, although quite recent attempts to introduce some species (e.g. the red deer) into these countries met with fair success. Most of these animals are hunted for sport, but some species kept as livestock are now so indispensable to man that he would be lost without them.

Hedgehog

Erinaceus europaeus

The hedgehog is a solitary animal with an unmistakable spiny coat covering the whole of its back and sides. We are most likely to encounter it after dusk. It is not over-cautious, as it knows that it can rely on its 16,000 spines for protection.

The hedgehog inhabits practically the whole of Europe and a large part of Asia. It chiefly frequents light, deciduous woods, parks and gardens and is not particularly shy of man. In central Europe it is found at altitudes of up to 2,000 m and further east even higher. During its nocturnal activities it looks for insects, larvae, pupae, earthworms, snails and slugs and may even catch lizards, mice or young birds, or steal the eggs of ground-nesting birds. Very occasionally it eats greenstuffs. For its size (length 25—30 cm), it has a huge appetite and consumes large amounts of food. It is also noted for catching snakes and it was found that a hedgehog is four times more resistant to snake venom than a guinea pig of the same size.

When hunting, it is guided mainly by its sense of smell, aided by hearing. Its vision plays a less important role.

Once or twice a year, the female gives birth to 2—10 young in a nest lined with moss, leaves and dry grass. The young are covered with soft, immature spines lying close to their body and are cared for by the female for about 40 days. The family then separates and each member ventures off on its own.

When winter approaches, the hedgehog retires to a burrow in the ground, thickly covered with fallen leaves, and hibernates. It stops eating, all its functions slacken and its body temperature falls almost to the environmental temperature (in severe winters it becomes stabilized at about +5°C).

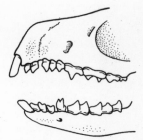

Hedgehog's dentition

Mole

Talpa europaea

The mole is well equipped for a subterranean existence. It has a cylindrical body, from which the wide, spade-like fore limbs, with their strong claws, project sideways, and it is covered with a plushy black coat. Its body is 125—160 mm long, while its tail measures 23—28 mm and its hind legs 17—19 mm. Most of its life is spent underground and it seldom emerges into the light. Its eyes, embedded in the skin, look like tiny poppy seeds. The ears have no auricle and their only protection is a low ridge of skin. Owing to their mode of life, therefore, moles have a very different body structure from other mammals.

About 5—30 cm below the surface, the mole builds a network of burrows, which it constantly extends. It pushes the unwanted soil out and it is this which forms the familiar mole-hills. The nest usually lies at a depth of 30—60 cm below the largest of these mounds. It is large and roomy and is lined with fine root-lets, leaves, grass, etc. Every mole has its own nest, but the system of underground passages may be inhabited by several individuals and may extend for a distance of 1 km.

The female rears only one litter of 2—7 young in a year. The young leave the nest at about 33 days, but still remain for some time in their mother's company.

The mole lives entirely on flesh. In times of shortage it lays in a stock of earthworms.

Moles can be found almost everywhere — at low and high altitudes, in fields and meadows and in forests. They inhabit practically the whole of Europe (their northerly limits are the south of Sweden and Scotland) and they extend east to Lake Baikal and Mongolia.

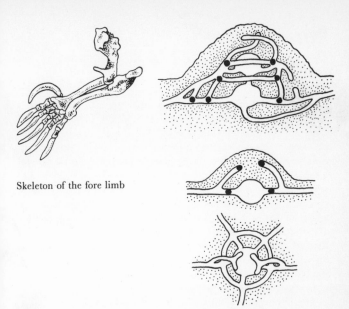

Skeleton of the fore limb

Mole's burrow

Pyrenean Desman

Desmana pyrenaicus

Moles
Talpidae

Outwardly, desmans somewhat resemble large shrews, but their anatomy shows that they are more closely related to moles and they were therefore included in the mole family. There are only two known species of these animals and in Europe their distribution is very limited. They have a compact, stocky body, a short neck and a long, mobile snout resembling a small trunk, which is constantly snuffling about in search of food. Both species live in or near water. With their thick, waterproof coat and their flat, webbed, five-toed feet, they are well equipped for an aquatic mode of life. Their peculiarly shaped tail is constricted at the base, swollen in the middle and flat-sided towards the tip. It has the function of a rudder. On their underside, near the base of their tail, desmans have a musk gland which secretes a substance with an acrid odour.

The Pyrenean desman inhabits clear mountain streams in the Pyrenees and the north of Spain and Portugal. Its body measures 11—13 cm, its tail is 13—15 cm long and it weighs 50—80 grammes. Its plushy coat is dark brown, with a metallic lustre on the back, silvery white on the abdomen and yellowish on the chest. Desmans catch their prey mainly in the water and eat almost any kind of small aquatic animals, including fish.

The related species, the Russian desman *(Desmana moschata)* is substantially larger (body length 18—21 cm, tail length 17—20 cm). Originally a native of the lower reaches of the Volga and the Don and the middle reaches of the Ural, it has been introduced into many other places in the European part of the USSR, where it is bred for its fur.

Hind limb

Common Shrew

Sorex araneus

Shrews
Soricidae

Shrews are often mistaken for mice, but mice are rodents, while shrews are insectivores and are thus related to hedgehogs and moles. Seen under a magnifying-glass, their teeth are more terrible than even those of beasts of prey. The members of the genus *Sorex* have 32 sharp-pointed, red-tipped teeth. The common shrew is very small (its body measures 65—85 mm and its hairy tail 32—56 mm), with a back the shade of tobacco and a light-coloured abdomen.

It is found at low and high altitudes, but mostly it frequents dank woods where there is an abundance of fallen trees, crevices, holes and moss-grown stones. Here it finds sufficient to eat — insects, spiders, slugs and worms. If the soil is soft, the common shrew may dig its own burrow, but it prefers abandoned vole or mouse holes and sometimes makes its nest in a hollow stump or between the roots of trees, often below the level of the ground. The nest is made of leaves, moss and grass. The female gives birth to 1—9 young three to four times a year. The young are born hairless and blind and do not open their eyes until the third week. They first venture from the nest at the age of 21 days and leave it for good on the 22nd or 23rd day. During the reproductive period, the males have well developed scent glands on their sides.

Shrews are relatively short-lived. They seldom see a second winter and under natural conditions die at about 14 months. They do not hibernate.

The common shrew inhabits Europe and Asia from the tundra to the deserts. It is absent in Ireland. In the temperate belt of these continents it occurs in large numbers in places where conditions are favourable.

Dentition

Pygmy Shrew

Sorex minutus

The pygmy shrew is one of the smallest mammals. Its body measures 40—64 mm and its relatively long, bushy tail 32—46 mm, while its weight is only 3—5 grammes. In colouring, it is similar to the common shrew, but is noticeably greyer. The two species can easily be differentiated by the condylobasal length of their skull, which is 18—20 mm in the common shrew, but only 14.5—16 mm in the pygmy shrew.

The pygmy shrew's distribution range extends from Ireland across Europe and Siberia to the Far East. It occurs mainly in deciduous and conifer woods, but is less abundant than the common shrew. The habits of the two species are very similar and they build similar nests. Reproduction occurs between April and September, during which the female gives birth to three or four litters of 2—9 young. The young do not leave the nest until they are 'grown up' and are practically the same as the parents in appearance. The pygmy shrew is no less of a glutton than the common shrew and dies within 5—9 hours if deprived of food. Insects and small invertebrates form its main diet. Our knowledge of the biology of this mammal is still incomplete.

Like the other members of the *Sorex* genus, the pygmy shrew is very fragile. A vole or mouse caught in a trap by its foot or tail is usually still alive and kicking when we find it, but a shrew (even if caught only by a toe) does not survive. A dead shrew will very often be found unhurt beside a closed trap, showing that it probably died from pure shock.

Dentition

Northern Shrew
or **Laxmann's Shrew**

Sorex caecutiens

The northern shrew is another species of the red-toothed *Sorex* genus. Its vast area of distribution stretches from northern Sweden, Norway and north-eastern Poland across the Eurasian tundra and taiga as far as the Chukot Peninsula, the Kurile Islands, Sakhalin and Japan. In the south it extends to Mongolia and China. Since it was fairly recently found in Holland, we can assume that it probably occurs in other parts of Europe as well. It is apparently often mistaken for the common shrew and, indeed, the two species are sometimes hard to tell apart. In size, the northern shrew comes between the common shrew and the pygmy shrew. Its body measures 54—67 mm, its tail 40—46 mm (about 70 per cent of its body length) and its hind paw 11—12 mm. It can be identified by the condylobasal length of its skull, which never exceeds 18 mm (16.2—17.7 mm). It is similarly coloured to the common shrew, as it has a dark brown or blackish brown back and a grey, russet-tinged abdomen.

The northern shrew is a tundra- and forest-dweller. It lives in damp spots rich in humus and mould, but shuns large peat-bogs. It has the same diet as the common shrew and reproduces throughout the warm part of the year. Like other shrews, its young, of which there are 2—11 in a litter, are born blind.

Greater attention ought to be paid to the incidence of this species in Europe, as it may occur in other parts as well as in the north.

Dentition

Alpine Shrew

Sorex alpinus

The alpine shrew is distributed mainly in the Alps, but also lives in the Pyrenees, the Harz Mountains, the Black Forest, Bavaria, the Bohemian Forest, the Giant Mountains, the Bohemian-Moravian uplands, the Carpathians and many ranges in the Balkans. It lives in mountain forests and frequents the dwarf (knee) pine zone. It is seldom found at such high altitudes, however, but often comes down to about 400 m. It prefers cold, shady spots, such as the weeds growing beside mountain streams and torrents or their sources. Its affinity for water is not as great as that of the water shrew, however. Its 32 red-pointed teeth show that it belongs to the genus *Sorex*. It can easily be identified by its black-grey coat, the white underside of its long tail and its light legs.

If a skull is available, we can recognize the alpine shrew from its dentition, as the first molar in the lower jaw has two cusps, whereas it has only one in the common shrew and the pygmy shrew. The alpine shrew's body measures 62—88 mm, its tail 60—75 mm and its hind paw 14—16 mm. The female produces about five young once or twice a year. The nest usually lies in an old burrow or among stones, but nests built in thick grass 10—20 cm above the ground have also been found. Our knowledge of the biology of the alpine shrew is still very incomplete.

Dentition

Water Shrew

Neomys fodiens

The aquatic forms which evolved among the insectivores include the water shrew, which measures 72—96 mm, has a 47—77 mm tail and hind paw 16—20 mm long. Members of the genus *Neomys* have 30 sharp teeth with red tips, as in the genus *Sorex*. The water shrew's coat is blackish grey or black on the back and silvery white or cream on the underside. Its adaptation to an aquatic existence is manifested in several of its characteristics. Its fine, velvety coat is thick, well greased and waterproof, so that a healthy specimen is dry as soon as it leaves the water.

Its relatively wide hind feet are edged with stiff bristles, which spread out like the teeth of a comb when the animal is swimming, turning the legs into paddles. A similar ridge of bristles is present on the underside of the tail, which thus forms an effective rudder. This animal is a good diver and can remain a long time under water.

In Europe, it is absent only in Ireland, Spain and the islands of the Mediterranean. In Asia, it extends to the Far East, keeping north of the steppes. It makes its nest near the waterside, between roots, in deserted burrows of other small mammals, or in holes which it digs for itself in soft soil. It reproduces all through the warm part of the year and generally has two or three litters of 2—9 young. The young are suckled for almost a whole month, but start taking solids before they are completely weaned. Water shrews live on small aquatic creatures, particularly insects. They also catch small fish. Like other shrews, they seldom survive a second winter and their mean life span is only eighteen months, despite the fact that they are much more hardy than the common shrew.

Dentition

Mediterranean Water Shrew

Neomys anomalus

The Mediterranean water shrew closely resembles the preceding species, but on close examination we can see a number of differences. In the Mediterranean water shrew, the bristles bordering the hind feet are much shorter, the tail is not so flat and the ridge of bristles on the tail is less well developed, showing that this species is not as well adapted for life in the water as its larger relative. The Mediterranean water shrew likes damp places with dense undergrowth, but is not restricted to either flowing or stagnant water and, in fact, it often lives far from open water. Swamps are its favourite habitat and they are the only places where it is sometimes found in large numbers.

Its distribution is intermittent. It inhabits central and southern Europe and Asia Minor and is found high up in the mountains (in central Europe up to 2,000 m). It is not found in northern Europe.

In colouring, it resembles the water shrew, but its coat has a silvery sheen on the back and its underside is always silvery white. It measures 47—60 mm and its hind paw, which measures 14—15.5 mm, is always shorter than that of the water shrew.

Our knowledge of the biology of this mammal is very limited. It usually nests underground, but in marshes it builds a spherical nest above the ground, in tangled aquatic plants. The female produces 5—6 young about twice a year.

Dentition

Bicoloured White-toothed Shrew

Crocidura leucodon

As distinct from members of the genera *Sorex* and *Neomys*, shrews of the genus *Crocidura* have white teeth, without red tips. Shrews of the genus *Sorex* have 32 teeth and members of the genus *Neomys* 30, while white-toothed shrews have only 28. The most distinctive feature of white-toothed shrews is their tail, however, as the normal, short hairs are thinly interspersed with long, light hairs.

The bicoloured white-toothed shrew measures 67—90 mm, its tail 30—40 mm and its hind paw 12—13 mm, while the condylobasal length of its skull is 18—20 mm. Its back is greyish brown to chocolate brown and its underside greyish white or white. The sharp dividing line between the two colours is an important identification mark.

This shrew is abundant in western and southern Europe except England, Spain and southern Italy, and it extends across the Caucasus, Iran, Kazakhstan and Turkestan up to central Siberia. In Europe, its northerly distribution stops roughly at latitude 53°, but here it is already rare. It chiefly inhabits lowlands and, unlike the members of the genus *Sorex*, it prefers dry places, such as bushy hillsides, hedges and the outskirts of deciduous woods. In the winter it shelters in hay-stacks and frequents human communities, where it is often to be found in cellars. Like other shrews, it lives on small animals.

Reproduction takes place from the spring to the autumn. After a gestation period of 31—33 days, the female gives birth to 3—9 young, which open their eyes at 13 days and at about 40 days are the same size as the parents. The bicoloured white-toothed shrew is active after dusk and during the night.

Dentition

Lesser White-toothed Shrew or **Scilly Shrew**

Crocidura suaveolens

The lesser white-toothed shrew is noticeably smaller than the preceding species. It has a greyish brown back and a light grey (sometimes yellowish) underside. Its body measures 50—75 mm, its tail is about half its body length, its hind paw is 10—12 mm long and the length of its skull is 16—18 mm. It inhabits most of Europe except the north and also occurs in Asia and Africa. In Europe, it is found in the same types of habitat as the bicoloured white-toothed shrew, but, in addition, it frequents damp, shady spots. In the mountains of central Europe it lives at altitudes of up to 1,600 m. The lesser white-toothed shrew makes its home in the vicinity of man more often than the bicoloured white-toothed shrew and in the winter it always seeks shelter in human communities. White-toothed shrews differ little in their habits. Their young leave the nest at the age of only 20 days and are soon independent. They feed on small animals.

White-toothed shrews have an interesting habit without any parallel among other mammals. This is the habit of walking in single file. When the young make their first excursions from the nest, the female places herself in a convenient position so that one of them can instinctively fasten its teeth in the hairs at the root of her tail. The rest then follow suit, each gripping the one in front with its teeth. Thus the female has no difficulty in getting them back to the nest again. The chain is so strong that even if the female is picked up the young do not let go. The cause of this habit is probably that young white-toothed shrews have very poor vision and could hardly find their way back to the nest alone. The female also carries the young by gripping them in her teeth by the skin of their back.

Dentition

Common European White-toothed Shrew

Shrews
Soricidae

Crocidura russula

Our data on the biology and distribution of this species is still incomplete. In general, it is common in western Europe and extends as far as the Elbe and the Ore Mountains in the west of Czechoslovakia. Early sources claim that it occurs in Czechoslovakia and Hungary, but it was shown that the authors concerned confused it with other species. It also lives in the Mediterranean region, North Africa, Asia Minor and central Asia and extends as far as Japan. In western Europe it has much the same habitats as the bicoloured white-toothed shrew, as it lives on the outskirts of woods, in gardens and sheds, beside rivers and streams and in meadows and fields. It also occurs quite high up in the mountains (up to 1,600 m in the Alps).

It resembles the bicoloured white-toothed shrew in size, but its underside is yellowish grey or greyish white (not white) and the brown-grey colouring of its back mingles with the lighter colouring of its underside without a dividing line. Its body measures 60—85 mm, its tail 30—46 mm and its hind paw 12—14 mm. As in the bicoloured white-toothed shrew, the condylobasal length of its skull is 18—20 mm.

The common European white-toothed shrew may have 2—4 litters a year, the 3—7 young being born after a gestation period of 28—31 days. It often lives in human dwellings and is even said to reproduce there during the winter. Like other white-toothed shrews, the young accompany the female in chain formation.

Dentition

Savi's Pygmy Shrew
or **Etruscan Shrew**

Suncus etruscus

Savi's pygmy shrew is classified in a different genus from the other European white-toothed shrews because it has a different number of teeth (30 instead of 28). The smallest mammal known, its body measures 34—48 mm, its tail 22—31 mm and its hind paw 6.8—8.1 mm. The condylobasal length of its skull is 12—12.6 mm and it weighs only 1.2—1.8 grammes. Its tail is thickly covered with sensory hairs, as in the genus *Crocidura*. The sensory hairs are coarse and straight, have a sensitive nerve ending at their root and possess a tactile function. This shrew has a yellowish grey or brownish grey back and a greyish white underside, so that it often appears to be all one colour. It is not a well-known mammal and we are more likely to find its remains in the gastric pellets ejected by owls than to actually catch it.

In Europe, Savi's pygmy shrew has so far been found only in the countries bordering the Mediterranean — Spain, the south of France, Italy, Greece, Yugoslavia and some of the islands in the Mediterranean. From here it extends to the Near East, central Asia, India, China, the Malayan Peninsula and Japan and it is also distributed in Africa.

It lives in warm, moist places, where it seeks the shade, and likes to frequent springs and the banks of streams and rivers, where it finds convenient shelter and an adequate food supply among the vegetation and under stones and roots. It has also been caught in reed beds near the coast.

Dentition

Greater Horseshoe Bat

Rhinolophus ferrumequinum

Horseshoe bats form a separate group (Microchiroptera), as the curious membranous outgrowths on their snout distinguish them from all other bats. They have 32 teeth.

The greater horseshoe bat is the largest member of the group in Europe. Its back is greyish or chocolate brown and its underside greyish white or cream. Its body measures 59—79.5 mm, its tail 60 mm and its forearm 54—60 mm. The condylobasal length of its skull varies from 20 to 22 mm. It inhabits wooded, hilly country. In the southern part of its area of distribution it is found at altitudes of up to 2,000 m. In the summer it frequents attics in old houses, old masonry and often caves. In the winter it sleeps in caves, galleries and cellars, hanging from the ceiling, almost entirely wrapped in its patagial membrane. It occurs in the temperate parts of southern Europe, including southern England, extends across Asia to Japan and is also found in North-west Africa.

In the reproductive period, the females form large, separate colonies. These are not the exclusive 'hen-parties' known among the majority of European species, however, as they include a relatively large proportion of males (20—30 per cent). The young are born in May or June, and at the end of September or in October the bats disperse to their regular winter quarters. Even today, we still have no satisfactory explanation of the impulse which causes horseshoe bats to fly every year to the same region and the same underground chambers. At the end of March or the beginning of April they wake from their winter sleep and return to their summer residence. When changing their dwelling they usually cover only short distances, although moves of over 100 km have been recorded. They live chiefly on moths, flies and beetles.

Detail of head

Long-eared Bat

Plecotus auritus

Typical Bats
Vespertilionidae

This relatively small bat is noted for its long ears. When it rests, its ears are folded under its wings, leaving only the tragus (a varyingly shaped membranous flap on the lower margin of the ear) showing. A few years ago, only one species of long-eared bat was thought to exist, but it was found that there were two, very similar species, both with 36 teeth. The newly discovered species was named southern bat; it is actually more abundant than the one for which it was often mistaken.

The rarer long-eared bat occurs more at high altitudes. It has a brownish grey or brownish yellow back, a white, ochre-tinged underside and is, in general, lighter than the southern bat. Its forearm measures 35.5—41.5 mm (males) or 37—41.2 mm (females). The condylobasal length of its skull (14.3—15.8 mm) is slightly smaller than in the southern bat.

The area of distribution of the long-eared bat has not been absolutely defined, but we know that it lives in England, the north of Spain, France, Holland, Belgium, Germany, Scandinavia, the north of Italy and the mountains of Bulgaria and that it extends across the middle of the USSR as far as Mongolia, Manchuria and Japan. In the summer, it sleeps in warm attics and in winter in cellars, deserted galleries, caves, sheltered corners of wood-sheds, etc. The females form small colonies in the summer, while the males live solitarily. These bats look for their winter quarters at the end of October or the beginning of November. As a rule, they are not found deep underground. At the end of March or the beginning of April they wake up and start hunting for food, at the same time returning to their summer residence. It was found that they have a life span of up to 12 years.

Ear shape

Caudal membrane

Brown Bat
or **Mouse-eared Bat**

Typical Bats
Vespertilionidae

Myotis myotis

The common feature of the typical bats, or vespertilionids, is that they have no membranous appendages on their snout. The number of their teeth varies from 32 to 38. The family as a whole is divided into several genera differentiated by their dentition.

The brown bat is both the largest and the commonest European bat. It has a greyish brown back, a light grey underside and greyish brown wings. Its terminal tail vertebrae project about 3 mm beyond its caudal patagial membrane. Its body measures 61—79 mm, its forearm 50—67 mm, its tail 51.5—63.2 mm and the condylobasal length of its skull is 21—24 mm.

The brown bat inhabits North Africa and a large part of Europe. It can be encountered both in mountains and lowlands and in the summer it frequents attics and towers, where it hangs from the ceiling, rafters, etc., or crawls into crevices. Sometimes it forms large colonies comprising up to 1,000 individuals. In the summer, the females rear the young in separate colonies, but in the winter males and females live together in caves, galleries and cellars, sometimes in large, tight clusters. The faeces which collect under such groups form excellent manure. The female gives birth to a single young, which at first lives clinging to the mother and is capable of independent flight after 45 days.

The brown bat can catch large insects, such as maybugs, on the wing.

The brown bat's winter quarters may be quite a long way away from its summer residence. Use of the ring-marking method showed that it can fly distances of up to 260 km. It uses the same winter shelter every year.

Caudal membrane

Barbastelle

Barbastella barbastellus

The barbastelle can be recognized immediately by its ears, which are joined at the base on their medial aspect. It is a small bat and its silky, almost black coat has a silvery lustre. It has relatively narrow wings and its tiny mouth is capable of catching only small insects. Its body measures 42—51.2 mm, its tail 42—49 mm, its forearm 37—41.5 mm and the condylo-basal length of its skull is 13—13.7 mm.

The northern limits of the barbastelle in Europe are England and southern Scandinavia, while in the east it extends beyond Lake Baikal. It is a common species in its area of distribution, where it chiefly inhabits wooded regions at high altitudes. In the summer it shelters in trees and buildings, in the winter in caves and galleries. Unlike other bats, it never hibernates in damp underground chambers, but always chooses dry spots. It hibernates tucked away in a crevice, or hanging from the wall or ceiling. Sometimes it forms large colonies, but is usually found singly in its winter quarters. The latter are near the entrance to underground spaces, as the barbastelle is highly resistant to low temperatures. It was already present in Europe by the end of the Ice Ages and is thus used to severe conditions, as seen from the case of a specimen found hibernating in sur-roundings where the environmental temperature was −14°C.

The female gives birth to the young in July or August, i.e. at a time when the young of other species can already fly. The barbastelle hunts on the outskirts of woods, in avenues and parks and does not like flying across wide, open spaces. It is a late hibernator so that it is not uncommon to see it still flying about in November.

Caudal membrane

Common Bat or Pipistrelle

Typical Bats
Vespertilionidae

Pipistrellus pipistrellus

The common bat is one of the smallest species. It has a dark brown back and only slightly lighter underside, while its wings and relatively small ears are so dark as to be almost black. Only half of the last tail vertebra projects beyond its caudal patagial membrane. Its body measures 33.5—48 mm, its tail 26—36 mm, its forearm 29—33.5 mm and the condylobasal length of its skull is only 11—12 mm.

This bat is distributed over the whole of Europe, Asia and North-west Africa. It is common at low altitudes and in places occurs at moderately high altitudes. It hibernates in protected spaces in buildings, caves and cellars and in the summer it shelters in hollow trees, nesting-boxes, cracks in wooden buildings or behind bark. Some of its colonies may comprise as many as 2,000 individuals. It flies fast and very skilfully, usually 15—20 m above the ground. Once a year, between May and July, the female gives birth to usually two (less frequently one or three) young, which are independent at the age of two months.

The common bat hibernates for a somewhat shorter time than other bats. In mild weather it will also hunt by day in the middle of the winter.

Use of the ring-marking method showed that these bats always hibernate in the same places and that to reach them they cover relatively long distances, sometimes in large swarms. A common bat marked in the southern Ukraine flew 1,150 km to southern Bulgaria — an extraordinary feat for a bat. Cases have also been described in which flocks of migrating bats rested for a night in human dwellings while on their way to their winter roosts.

Caudal membrane

Serotine

Eptesicus serotinus

The serotine is a comparatively large species with extremely wide wings. It has a dark brown back, a light brown underside and very dark ears and wings. The length of its ears is only slightly greater than their width. The tip of its tail projects 5—7 mm beyond its caudal patagial membrane. Its body measures 64—78 mm, its tail 44—57 mm, its forearm 48—56.3 mm and the condylobasal length of its skull is 18.4—20.5 mm.

The serotine inhabits Europe (where its northern limits are southern England and Denmark), Asia and North-west Africa. It is one of the commonest species. In the summer it usually shelters in attics or walls, where it may be found tucked away in a crack, or under the roof. It hibernates mostly in cellars and closets, but occasionally in caves and hollow trees, usually not far from its summer residence. Its flying ability corresponds to its wide, blunt-tipped wings, since it flies clumsily, fairly close to the ground. It does not come out to hunt until long after dusk. In May and June the females form separate colonies comprising, as a rule, only a few dozen individuals, although colonies numbering several hundreds have also been reported. The female gives birth to two (only seldom one) young. As soon as the young are independent, the female colonies break up and the males and females form mixed colonies again.

The serotine is relatively easy to keep in captivity and has few requirements.

Caudal membrane

Noctule Bat

Nyctalus noctula

Typical Bats
Vespertilionidae

The noctule bat is one of the large species. It has a reddish brown or yellowish brown back, a slightly lighter underside and a short, thick, glossy coat. Its wings are very long and narrow and it has a round, short head with a 'bulldog' face. Its ears are set wide apart.

Its body measures 61.5—80 mm, its tail 43—53 mm, its forearm 50.5—56.5 mm and the condylobasal length of its skull is 17.4—19.4 mm.

The noctule bat inhabits practically the whole of Europe and Asia except the most northerly parts. It also occurs on the Malayan Peninsula. It abounds wherever there are sufficient hollow trees, in which we can find it both in summer and in winter. If the supply of natural roosts is inadequate, it contents itself with the attics of tall buildings. Its summer colonies comprise 20—30 individuals, while in its winter roost there may be several hundred.

The noctule bat flies fast and skilfully, high above the ground. It starts to hunt while it is still light and we may catch sight of it high up among swallows and martins. It was found, by marking it with rings, that it migrates for very long distances. For instance, a noctule bat marked near Riga (Latvia, USSR) on August 21, 1949, was caught near Česká Lípa in northern Bohemia in the same year. Numerous observations on favourable autumn days indicate that these bats evidently migrate regularly.

Mating occurs either in the autumn or in the spring. In May or June, the female gives birth to one or two young in the company of other females, in their summer residence. For the first few days the young cling to the female. On the sixth or seventh day they open their eyes and at five weeks they undertake their first independent flight.

Caudal membrane

Brown Hare or **European Hare**

Hares and Rabbits
Leporidae

Lepus europaeus

The body of the European hare measures 60—70 cm, its tail only 8—10 cm, and its body weight varies from 3—6.5 kg. Its coat is cinnamon brown, with a lighter underside and a white abdomen, and it has long, black-tipped ears. Its hind legs are much longer and stronger than the fore legs, so that it hops instead of walking. It can develop a speed of up to 70 km an hour. When hopping, the whole sole of its hind feet touches the ground, but it runs only on its toes.

The hare is a solitary animal except at mating time, when the males seek the company of females and actually fight each other. Each hare inhabits a separate area, which it continuously demarcates with a substance secreted by a few scent glands localized chiefly near its anus and on its face. When the hare cleans itself, the substance secreted by the facial glands sticks to its paws and is in this way transferred to the ground.

Originally, the hare was a native of Europe (except Ireland and the Iberian Peninsula) as far as the Urals, central Asia, Asia Minor and East and South Africa. In Asia it is spreading further east and also, with advances in agriculture, further north. It occurs in all types of country except the highest mountains and large fir forests, but is commonest in lowland agricultural regions.

Hares are very prolific and some years the female may produce up to five litters of 2—4 young. As distinct from rabbits, young hares are born with open eyes and a furry coat, while the female makes an open nest and does not hide the young in a burrow.

Hares are herbivorous. They live on greenstuff and in the winter they also gnaw the bark of young trees.

Young in its first week

Mountain Hare

Lepus timidus

Hares and Rabbits
Leporidae

The mountain hare is sturdier than the brown hare, but the two are closely related and often inter-breed. The mountain hare measures 44—74 cm and weighs 3—5.5 kg. It has shorter ears and its size displays considerable geographical variability. In summer its coat is brown, brownish grey or ochre, but in winter it turns pure white, except for its black-tipped ears. It has a short, round scut, which is grey on top in the summer. In some areas, only part of the population turns white (e.g. Scandinavia and Scotland), while in Ireland it never displays a white coat.

The mountain hare lives in northern Europe and Asia, where towards the east, the southern limits of its distribution are pushing markedly southwards. It also occurs in the north of North America. A variety preserved in the Alps is a relic of the Ice Ages. Another variety, similarly produced by geographical isolation, is found in England and Ireland.

The female gives birth to two (in Asia three) litters of 5—8 young a year, in a depression in the ground under a bush, and rears them in the same way as the brown hare. The mountain hare population undergoes very pronounced changes. In some years the countryside swarms with them, while in others they seem to have died out altogether. In the north of the Siberian taiga they over-proliferate every 8—12 years, in the forests of the European part of the USSR every 4—9 years. The mountain hare eats different herbs and its diet also includes a large pro- portion of woody plants.

In the Alps it inhabits the belt from the upper limits of the forest down to 3,000 m; in the winter it descends to somewhat lower altitudes.

Wild Rabbit

Oryctolagus cuniculus

Hares and Rabbits
Leporidae

The wild rabbit differs from the hare in various respects, but chiefly in size. Its body measures 40—50 cm, its scut only 5—7 cm. An adult specimen weighs 1.5—2 kg. Its relatively shorter ears are not black-tipped and it has a more compact body and shorter legs. Its colouring is also different. Its coat is greyer, without any russet tones, while its underside is greyish white. We can also tell a running rabbit from a hare by the pure white underside of its scut. Unlike the hare, the rabbit can dig, as seen from its massive fore paws. In places where it is present in large numbers, the ground is riddled with its burrows. Since rabbits live in colonies, the burrows are always built accordingly, in the form of warrens.

The wild rabbit originally came from a very limited area comprising Spain, the Balearic Islands and the Atlas Mountains (North Africa). It was evidently spread by man as a domestic animal, but often escaped and turned wild again. It settled in a large part of western and central Europe.

It was also introduced into other parts of the world and in some places it became a scourge, the classic example being Australia, where it had virtually no natural enemies. In central Europe the female produces 3—5 litters, each containing 6—8 (and sometimes up to 12) young a year in special short nursery burrows in thickets and at the margin of woods. These burrows, which are not very deep, terminate in an oval chamber lined with wool plucked from the female's belly. For the first ten days the young are blind and when the female leaves the burrow she blocks up the entrance.

The wild rabbit strips the area round its burrows of all the vegetation within reach, including young tree shoots as well as herbs.

Young in its first week

Flying Squirrel

Pteromys volans

Squirrels
Sciuridae

This is the only European rodent adapted for simple gliding flight. Between its fore and hind limbs it has a membrane, covered with fine fur, which is pulled taut by its limbs as it leaps from tree to tree and, together with its bushy tail, moderates its fall like a parachute. The flying squirrel can thus jump much better than the true squirrels and may land far from the foot of the tree from which it takes off.

In appearance and size it resembles a dormouse rather than a squirrel. Its large eyes denote it as a twilight and nocturnal animal. Its ash-grey, brown-tinged back has a silvery sheen in winter and its underside is silvery white. Its body measures 135—205 mm, its bushy tail 90—140 mm, its hind paw 30 to 39 mm and its ear, which is not tufted, 15—21 mm. The condylobasal length of its skull is about 37 mm.

The flying squirrel is a typical arboreal animal. It is wonderfully nimble in the trees, but it moves awkwardly on the ground. It inhabits the spreading forests of Scandinavia and Siberia, where it prefers mixed growths with plenty of alders and birches, as it eats their seeds. During the daytime it hides in hollow trees and also builds nests for the young in them. Sometimes it even settles in nesting-boxes near human communities. It is very sensitive to environmental changes and as soon as man encroaches on its habitat, e.g. by cutting down old trees, it disappears. That is probably why the limits of its distribution in north-eastern Europe are steadily receding eastwards.

The flying squirrel produces two litters a year — in the spring and summer. The gestation period is about five weeks and there are usually 2—6 young in a litter. In the winter it sleeps in hollow trees.

Red Squirrel

Sciurus vulgaris

Most rodents are terrestrial animals, but the red squirrel is adapted to an arboreal mode of life. Its salient features are its long, bushy tail, its tufted ears and its agility in the trees. Its sharp claws enable it to hold on to relatively smooth bark, it can balance on the thinnest twigs and can jump nimbly from branch to branch.

There are several colour varieties of red squirrel — russet, brown, black and even tricolour (black, russet and white). It is not uncommon for two colour varieties to live in the same wood, but, in general, dark types are found in the mountains, while those which live in the lowlands are mainly russet. All of them have a white underside.

The red squirrel is primarily herbivorous, but its diet varies with the season. The best time of year for it is the autumn, when fruit and nuts, etc., are abundant. In the winter it usually eats the seeds of forest trees. When food is short, e.g. in the early spring, it gnaws young spruce, and sometimes pine, shoots. Occasionally it enriches its diet with flesh. When food is plentiful, squirrels have a habit of storing it.

In its own area, the red squirrel builds several spherical nests, which are usually made of twigs, grass and leaves and are placed high up in the tops of trees. The best made nest is used as a nursery.

Squirrels reproduce from the spring to the autumn. The female produces 1—3 litters of 3—7 young a year. They are born hairless and blind and do not open their eyes for four weeks. Red squirrels remain active even during the winter. They inhabit forests, parks and gardens all over Europe and in the mountains they ascend to the upper forest and shrub limit.

Skull viewed from above

Grey Squirrel

Sciurus carolinensis

Squirrels
Sciuridae

The grey squirrel was originally a native of the east of North America, but today no list of European mammals would be complete without it. Several times between 1876 and 1929 it was imported in large numbers to the British Isles (perhaps simply because of its friendliness and pretty appearance) and in the course of time it colonized wooded areas over about half of England and Scotland and a quarter of Ireland. It was also introduced, in a similar manner, into South Africa. It is now quite common in England, but its introduction there has had somewhat unfortunate consequences. Although its friendliness and tameness make it an attractive addition to parks and gardens, it has less endearing properties. It bites off the young shoots and buds of many economically important trees, eats their seeds and fruits, does damage to tree nurseries and crops and raids birds' nests. It also competes more successfully for food than the white-tailed variety of the red squirrel in the woods. Consequently, it is regarded as a serious pest and its numbers have to be regulated by planned shooting and other methods.

The grey squirrel is larger than the red squirrel. Its body measures 200—250 mm, its tail 190—200 mm and its weight ranges from 340 to 680 g. In both winter and summer its underside is white, while its back is grey, tinted with pink, in the winter and more of a brown shade in the summer. Its ears are not tufted.

It builds nests similar to those of the red squirrel and produces two litters, each with 1—7 young, in a year.

Ground Squirrel
or **European Souslik**

Citellus citellus

Although closely related to the true squirrels, the ground squirrel is a typical terrestrial rodent. It prefers warm lowlands and temperate uplands, where it lives in dry, steppe country and fields.

The back of its sandy, yellowish grey coat is marked with indistinct light spots and its underside is plain yellow. Its tail, which is much less bushy than that of a true squirrel, is relatively short (about one third of its body length). Its body measures 19—22 cm.

Ground squirrels live in colonies. Very often, especially in times of over-proliferation, we find places where the ground is riddled with their burrows. Near inhabited burrows we can always find faeces, but practically no loose soil, because, as they dig, the animals remove it in their facial pouches and dispose of it in the surrounding area. The nest chamber at the end of the burrow is usually lined with dry grass, chaff and other soft material. Once or twice a year, the female gives birth to 5—8 young in the nest.

The ground squirrel is largely herbivorous. Its staple food is seeds, but it also eats the green parts of plants. It supplements this diet with large insects, mice and even young birds and eggs.

Ground squirrels scurry along with their body close to the ground. Like most steppe animals, they sit up and 'beg' when looking about them.

The ground squirrel's area of distribution stretches from the steppes of eastern and south-eastern Europe across Bohemia to the western slopes of the Ore Mountains — the most westerly point of its incidence in Europe. In Asia, it extends to Mongolia and northern China.

Alpine Marmot

Marmota marmota

In appearance, the marmot resembles a large ground squirrel. When adult, it measures 70−90 cm, 13−16 cm of which is accounted for by its tail. Its short, smooth coat is yellowish brown to dark brown on the back and rusty yellow on the underside. The marmot is a typical mountain-dweller and lives in the Alps, the Carpathians and the mountains of central Asia. It has been introduced also into the Low Tatras, the Black Forest, the Pyrenees and parts of the Alps, where it was formerly absent. It inhabits the dwarf (knee) pine zone above the forest belt, at altitudes of 1,700 to 3,000 m. We can only occasionally catch a glimpse of it in grassy spots or among rocks and are more likely to hear the penetrating whistle which it uses to warn its fellows of danger.

The marmot is very skilled at digging and in stony ground it can excavate a burrow ten metres long at a depth of up to three metres. Most of the openings to its burrows lie under boulders. The burrows, which are long and wide, are used for hibernation.

The marmot's winter sleep lasts for over half a year. Before the winter sets in, the marmot feeds itself until it is covered with a thick layer of subcutaneous fat and weighs anything up to 6 kg. In April, when it wakes, it is weak and thin, but it quickly gains weight again and at the end of May or the beginning of June 2−6 blind young are born in the nest.

The marmot is an essentially diurnal animal, preferring fine, sunny weather. Its senses are highly developed and its vision and hearing in particular are unusually keen. Like the ground squirrel, it supplements its vegetarian diet with flesh. It attains sexual maturity in its second year and in favourable circumstances can live 15−18 years.

110

Skull viewed from above

European Beaver

Castor fiber

The European beaver is a robust rodent up to 1 m long and weighing up to 30 kg. It has a relatively high head and its horizontally flattened tail is hairy at the base, but is otherwise covered with scales. Its webbed hind feet, its occlusible nostrils and its thick, waterproof coat show that it is an aquatic animal. Its dark brown, glossy fur is fine and silky.

The beaver has a large anal gland, which in the Middle Ages was supposed to have miraculous healing powers. This superstition, together with the beaver's valuable coat, led to its being exterminated in many parts of Europe. The last European beavers now live in a few places on the middle reaches of the Elbe in Germany, on the Rhône in France and in a few places in Poland, Scandinavia and the USSR.

Although the beaver lives mainly on different aquatic plants, it also eats sugar beet, potatoes, maize and the bark of trees.

Its roomy burrow, which has several exits and a chamber in the centre, is excavated in a bank. The lair is lined with reeds, grass and wood chips. Beavers build large 'lodges' made of branches and twigs, faced with turf and soil, on stagnant water. These are sometimes huge, strong structures. The beavers keep the water at a constant level by constructing great dams, for which they even fell moderately large trees. With their sharp teeth they gnaw the trunk, making a V-shaped notch round its whole circumference, until the tree falls. The dam is reinforced with turf and soil and forms a small lake.

At the beginning of August, the female gives birth to 2—4 young, which are immediately able to see. Beavers are excellent swimmers and can remain under water for 10—14 minutes.

Footprints

Common Dormouse

Glis glis

With its bushy tail, the common dormouse looks like a little grey squirrel, but its ears are not tufted. Its body measures 13—18 cm, its tail 11—15 cm. We can tell by its large, dark eyes that it is a twilight and nocturnal animal. During the daytime it shelters in hollow trees, rock crevices or birds' nesting-boxes and does not wake until after sunset. As a result, few people are aware of it. Its local incidence is quite high, but it occurs only in warm regions and is absent in high mountains. It inhabits deciduous woods, orchards and parks. In the night it visits the attics of houses and cottages, raids larders and nibbles fruit, jam and nuts. Otherwise, dormice eat the seeds of trees, berries and insects and sometimes catch young birds and steal eggs. They hold their food in their fore paws, like squirrels.

In the autumn, when food is abundant, they grow fat, i.e. they form a layer of subcutaneous fat, on which they subsist when hibernating. In September or October they retire to a hole in the ground or a tree, curl up in a tight ball, with their tail covering their head, and sleep until April. About a month later, when they have put on a little weight again, they find a mate and build a nest. The nest is made of grass, leaves and moss and is situated in a hollow, or directly on a branch, in the open. Here, once a year, the female gives birth to 2—7 young, which in roughly three months are the same size as their parents.

The common dormouse's area of distribution ranges from northern Spain across southern, central and eastern Europe to Asia Minor and Transcaucasia. It was introduced into England artificially.

Garden Dormouse

Eliomys quercinus

The garden dormouse is the most brightly coloured member of the family. Its back is greyish brown, tinged with red, and its underside is white. Its cheeks are marked with black stripes and its light-coloured tail, which is brown on top, has a black tip and terminates in a bushy tuft. Its body measures 110—150 mm, its tail 100—120 mm and its hind paw 25—31 mm. Its area of distribution is larger than that of the edible dormouse, as it also lives in North Africa, southern and central Europe as far as the Urals and extends in the north to the islands of southern Finland. It occurs at low altitudes in deciduous and mixed woods, parks and gardens, but is most numerous in warm lowland areas. Nowhere is it very abundant. It ventures into human dwellings, where it occasionally steals stored fruit. Like the other members of the family, it is a nocturnal animal. It lives on fruit, berries and small animals and is the greatest flesh-eater among the dormice. It also spends more time on the ground than other species and frequents rubble, the maze of spaces under boulders and weathered rocks, where it may build its nest in a crevice. It also nests in trees, old birds' and squirrels' nests, tree hollows and nesting-boxes. The nest in which it hibernates is usually very warm and lined with soft material. Soon after waking from its winter sleep, the garden dormouse mates and between the end of May and July the female gives birth to one or two litters of 2—7 young, which do not open their eyes for 21 days. The garden dormouse makes purring or croaking sounds, which can often be heard.

Upper molars (left)
and lower molars (right)

Tree Dormouse

Dryomys nitedula

In size, the tree dormouse comes mid-way between the common dormouse and the garden dormouse. Its body measures 86—120 mm, its tail 60—113 mm. Its back is yellowish brown or greyish brown and its underside is white. Unlike the garden dormouse, the whole of its tail is bushy and has no black margins, while the black bar across its eyes distinguishes it from the common dormouse. In Europe, it occurs in the Bavarian Forest and further east, but the region where it is really plentiful is Slovakia. In central Europe it mainly inhabits deciduous and mixed woods at high altitudes and in places it ascends to the upper limit of the forest belt (e.g. in the Tatras). It has also been found in northern Italy and in the Balkans it is actually abundant at high and moderately high altitudes. Here, it inhabits deciduous woods, hedges, vineyards and dry places with only a few, sparse shrubs. To the east it extends across the Near East to the Altai Mountains.

Like other dormice, it lives chiefly on fruit and berries, occasionally supplemented by small animals, which it hunts after dusk and during the night. It is equally agile on the ground and in the trees. It usually nests in tree hollows or crevices in rocks, but sometimes builds its nest on a branch up to 12 m above the ground, or uses deserted birds' nests. During the reproductive period (April to August) the female gives birth to 1—2 litters of 2—5 young. In the northern parts of its area of distribution it hibernates (roughly from October until the beginning of April), but in the south it is active the whole year round.

Upper molars (left) and lower molars (right)

Hazel Mouse

Muscardinus avellanarius

Dormice
Gliridae

The hazel mouse is the smallest and most striking member of the dormouse family. It cannot be mistaken for any other species. Its body measures 75—88 mm and its tail, which is hairy, but not bushy, measures 55—77 mm. Its beautiful large, dark eyes indicate that it is a nocturnal animal.

The hazel mouse is distributed over practically the whole of Europe, from England and the Pyrenees in the west to the Volga in the east. In the north it extends to the south of Sweden and it also lives in Asia Minor. Its occurrence in central Europe is sporadic and it is absent in warm, fertile lowlands. In foothills and mountains it is less rare and in the Carpathians it has actually been found at the upper limit of the dwarf (knee) pine zone, at an altitude of 1,800 m. It inhabits both deciduous and mixed woods, while in the mountains it lives in conifer forests and the dwarf timber belt.

It usually builds its neat little nest in the branches of small trees and bushes, about one metre above the ground, but sometimes in grass, bilberry plants, raspberry canes or directly on the ground. Its winter nests lie just below the surface of the ground, in a crack or a layer of leaves. Sometimes several individuals may be found hibernating in the same nest. Once a year the female gives birth to 3—7 young, which are independent in about 35 days. The common dormouse has a life span of up to 7 years.

In the spring it initially lives on the buds of trees, the bark of young tree shoots, seeds, beechnuts and acorns. In the summer it eats wild strawberries, bilberries and raspberries. It supplements this diet with a small amount of flesh.

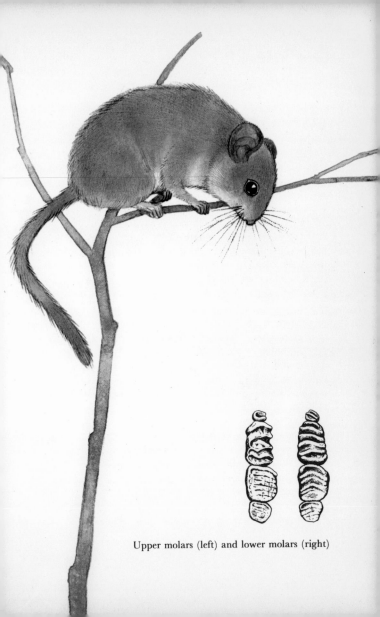

Upper molars (left) and lower molars (right)

Northern Birch Mouse

Sicista betulina

Birch Mice
Zapodidae

The northern birch mouse is a very remarkable animal. According to the rules of systematic zoology it is related to the jerboa family (Dipodidae). It is thus related to the steppe and desert rodents which have long hind legs and usually jump like little kangaroos. The hind legs of the northern birch mouse are not much longer than its fore legs, however, and at first glance it looks like a small, long-tailed mouse. Its body measures 50—75 mm, its tail (which is half as long again) 76—109 mm, and the condylobasal length of its skull is 16.2—18.8 mm. It has a yellowish grey back, a light grey underside and a distinctive narrow, dark stripe running from between its eyes to the base of its tail. Its upper lip is not cleft, as it is in mice.

In central Europe it is primarily a mountain-dweller, while to the north and east it also occurs in lowland forests and even in steppes. In the extreme east it inhabits the whole of Siberia to beyond Lake Baikal. It was only quite recently discovered in the mountains of central Europe. It spends most of its time on the ground, but is very adept at climbing low bushes, where it twines its long tail round the stems to keep its balance. Its summer nest is built in grass or moss, between the roots of bushes, under fallen trees or in rotting tree-stumps. From October to April it hibernates, curled up in a nest in a hole which it excavates itself just below the surface of the ground. Once a year the female gives birth to 2—6 young which develop relatively slowly and are suckled for five weeks.

The northern birch mouse's diet consists of grass seeds, small berries and insects.

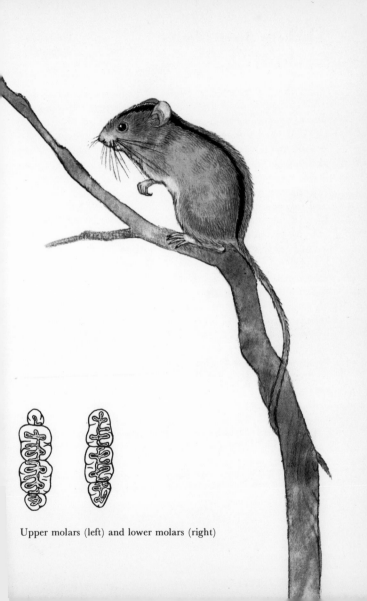

Upper molars (left) and lower molars (right)

Southern Birch Mouse

Sicista subtilis

Birch Mice
Zapodidae

This species is closely related to the northern birch mouse. It likewise has a yellowish grey coat, but its narrow, dark dorsal stripe is bordered by wider light stripes. Its body length is usually about 60 mm (but never more than 72 mm) and its tail is only one third longer than its body. The most westerly point of its area of distribution is Lake Neusiedler in Austria. It extends roughly from the plains of Hungary, across Rumania and the southern half of the European part of the USSR, to Kazakhstan and north-western China. It is a typical inhabitant of lowland and wooded steppes, where it lives among grass and herbs, in scrub and even in fields, both in dry places and near water. It does not dig its own summer burrows, but lives in the empty burrows of other rodents, in cracks in trees and under the roots of trees and bushes. Insects, seeds and the green parts and roots of plants form its staple diet.

Like other rodents, it evidently over-proliferates from time to time, but because of its secretive mode of life it goes unnoticed. As a result, there are many gaps in our knowledge of its biology. During the reproductive period, which lasts from May to the beginning of June, the female probably gives birth only once to 4—7 young. The southern birch mouse hibernates in burrows which it digs itself not very far below the surface of the ground.

Both species of birch mice (northern and southern) are easy to keep in captivity. The best way to catch them is to embed wide-necked bottles or drums in the ground. The animals fall into these without injuring themselves, but are unable to climb out again.

Lesser Mole Rat

Spalax leucodon

Mole Rats
Spalacidae

Several species of the rodent order have become adapted to an underground existence. One of these is the lesser mole rat, whose mode of life is reflected in the peculiar shape of its body and its internal organization. Its cylindrical body, which in fully grown specimens measures 190—230 mm, is covered with short, silky, greyish brown fur. Its tail and ears are completely invisible. It has a wide, flat head and a row of hard, stiff bristle-like whiskers grows from its cheeks. Its stumpy legs are not particularly well adapted for digging, like those of the mole, for example. They have five digits and the fore limbs, which are stronger than the hind limbs, have longer claws. The mole rat is genuinely blind, as its eyes are covered with skin and do not function.

The lesser mole rat lives in Hungary, the Balkans, the west of the Ukraine, Asia Minor and Transcaucasia, where it is found at both low and high altitudes. It betrays its presence by the huge mounds of earth (much larger than mole-hills) which it throws up when excavating its underground passages. Mole rats live singly in a maze of burrows not far below the surface of the ground. Only their winter burrows go down to any real depth (about 2 m). When digging, they use their large rodent teeth to remove obstacles. They loosen the soil with their powerful forehead, scoop it up with their flat-topped head and only sweep it aside with their fore paws. Small stocks of food, e.g. fragments of roots, tubers and the green parts of plants, are often to be found in their passages. Roots are their staple diet.

Mole rats reproduce only once a year, the female giving birth to 2—4 young in an underground nest lined with dry grass.

Skull — side view

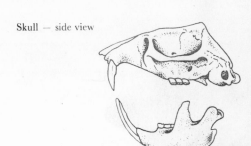

House Mouse

Mus musculus

Old World Rats and Mice
Muridae

The appearance of the house mouse is very variable and in Europe alone there are two distinct forms. In western Europe, the tail of the house mouse is the same length as its body, but the further east we go, the more its relative length diminishes. At the same time, its colouring also changes. West European mice are darker, while as we go east they acquire a yellowish tinge and their grey abdomen becomes lighter. In addition, the colouring of populations living in the vicinity of man (commensal populations) usually differs from that of house mice living in the open; zoologists distinguish several races on the basis of these characters.

The house mouse has a dark grey, brownish grey or yellowish grey back and a light grey, greyish white or yellowish grey underside. Its body measures 80—90 mm, its hind leg 16 to 18.5 mm and its skull 17—21 mm. As distinct from field mice and harvest mice, the house mouse has a sharp notch on the posterior margin of its upper rodent teeth and also differs from other species in respect of its unmistakable, disagreeable odour.

The house mouse is a cosmopolitan animal and occurs all over the world. Its original home was probably the Near East and from here, in both prehistoric and historic times, it was spread in grain. House mice living in the open are vegetarians and subsist mainly on seeds, while commensal populations are omnivorous and are capable of reproduction on a one-sided type of diet. They reproduce mainly in the spring and summer, but often also litter in the winter. The female thus produces several litters of 4—8 young in a year. By the age of 30 days the young are independent. They mature very quickly and within a year can have young of their own.

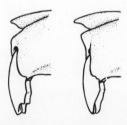

Incisors in field mouse (right)
and house mouse (left)

Harvest Mouse

Micromys minutus

The harvest mouse is about the same size as the northern birch mouse, but it has a shorter tail, lacks the dorsal stripe and its coat is redder. Its body measures 50—75 mm, tail 50—60 mm and its hind paw 12—16 mm. In the summer, adult specimens have a pretty, light russet coat, while young individuals and adults in their winter coat are greyish brown. Their underside is always white or cream, however. They can climb twigs, blades of grass, rushes and cereal plants with great skill, keeping their balance by means of their prehensile tail and the first toe of their hind foot, which can be opposed to the other digits.

The harvest mouse's area of distribution ranges from France and England across the whole of Europe and Asia as far as Japan and North Vietnam. Its incidence in Europe, where it occurs mainly in damp plains and foothills, is sporadic. Its nest resembles a bird's nest rather than a rodent's. It is usually woven between rushes and grass blades, while in fields it may be suspended from the stems of cereals or rape plants, 25—80 cm above the ground. The nest is spherical and has a side entrance. Sleeping nests have two openings, nursery nests only one. The finished nest, which is made of leaves shredded by the mouse's sharp teeth, is no larger than a baby's fist. In addition to these hanging nests, the harvest mouse makes underground nests in which it spends the cold season. In the winter it also retreats to solitary buildings standing in fields and very often it seeks shelter in hay-stacks.

The harvest mouse is very prolific and produces up to three litters of 3—7 young in a year. It is thus not surprising that it over-proliferates in favourable years.

Striped Field Mouse

Old World Rats and Mice
Muridae

Apodemus agrarius

The most conspicuous feature of this mouse is the almost black, sharply defined stripe running from its forehead down the middle of its back to the base of its tail. As distinct from the birch mouse, the stripe does not start between its eyes, but roughly in a line with the front of its ears. Compared with other field mice it has a relatively short tail (about three quarters the length of its body), short ears and small eyes. Its body measures 90—115 mm, its hind paw 18—21 mm. The condylobasal length of its skull is 18.5—26 mm. Its back is reddish brown, its underside greyish white.

The striped field mouse's area of distribution extends from the Rhineland across central and southern Europe to China, Korea and Japan. It lives in scrub country, near the edge of woods, beside streams, etc. It prefers damp spots and not infrequently lives in reed-beds. While it leads a similar life to other field mice, it is less gifted at climbing and jumping and is also more of a diurnal animal. Although it is mainly a vegetarian, its diet includes a large proportion of flesh. It digs an intricate maze of burrows, in which its leafy nest usually lies at a depth of about 40 cm. During the reproductive period (April to August) it produces 3—4 litters of 4—9 young.

Like other small rodents, the striped field mouse sometimes multiplies on a huge scale. The mice then retire in the winter to hay-stacks, where they find shelter, warmth and scraps of grain. They also invade barns and other farm buildings and in such years are quite as much of a pest as other mice.

Right fore and hind feet

Yellow-necked Field Mouse

Old World Rats and Mice
Muridae

Apodemus flavicollis

The yellow-necked field mouse is a slightly larger replica of the long-tailed field mouse. Its body length (90—120 mm) is sometimes the same, its tail is roughly the same length as its body, but its hind paw (24—26 mm) is usually longer than that of the other species. In addition, the dividing line between the rusty brown of its back and the white of its underside is very sharp. It is distinguished by a yellow spot, which can be either large or small, on its throat. The condylobasal length of its skull varies from 24—29 mm.

The yellow-necked field mouse inhabits practically the whole of Europe and Asia, except for their most southerly parts. In England and Denmark it is more abundant than the long-tailed field mouse. It inhabits both deciduous and conifer woods and seeks shelter in human dwellings in the winter. The yellow-necked field mouse climbs nimbly and we can sometimes find its nest in a tree hollow. Otherwise it digs burrows in the same types of places as the long-tailed field mouse. It lives mainly on seeds and has a preference for those containing oil, but it also eats a large proportion of flesh.

The yellow-necked field mouse is a nocturnal animal. It comes out to look for food about one hour after sundown, but may also be seen during the day. In the winter, tracks in the snow show that it undertakes long journeys (up to several hundred metres) from its burrow.

The yellow-necked field mouse reproduces in the same way as the long-tailed field mouse, but may also litter during the winter. Its normal life span is about eighteen months and it is exceptional for it to live 2—3 years.

Right fore and hind feet

Long-tailed Field Mouse

Old World Rats and Mice
Muridae

Apodemus sylvaticus

It is difficult to give a general characterization of the occurrence of this abundant rodent in Europe. Although in some languages it is described as a 'forest' mouse, it hardly ever occurs deep in the large forests of central Europe, but is regularly found on the outskirts of woods, in hedges, in the vegetation beside streams and rivers and near human communities. In southern Europe it is a normal part of the forest fauna, however. In the winter it seeks shelter in houses.

Its coat is greyish brown, with a faint russet tinge. On its sides, there is no sharp dividing line between this colour and the dingy white of its underside. As a rule (but not always), it has a narrow yellow bar on its white throat. It has large ears and large, dark eyes. Its body measures 90—105 mm, its tail 90—100 mm. The condylobasal length of its skull varies from 22—26 mm. Its hind paw (20—23 mm) enables it to take comparatively long leaps as it runs.

Since the seeds of trees and other plants are its staple diet, in times of over-proliferation it can do immense damage to tree nurseries and grain crops (and in granaries and larders). It does not hibernate, but during severe frosts may fall into a kind of torpor.

The females mature very young and litter in the same year in which they were born. In a year, one female can have 3, or possibly 4, litters of 2—8 young.

The long-tailed field mouse inhabits practically the whole of Europe (except the most northerly parts), North Africa, southern Siberia, Asia Minor and the Near East and India.

Right fore and hind feet

Black Rat
or Ship Rat

Old World Rats and Mice
Muridae

Rattus rattus

The black rat is much rarer in central Europe than the brown rat. The two are often confused, but in fact they are very different. In general, the black rat is smaller and slimmer (160—235 mm), its tail is usually the same length as its body or slightly longer and if its ears are curved over they reach its eyes or even cover them. Its hind paw measures 36—40 mm and its skull 36—44 mm. Two forms of this rat, with different colouring, exist. In black populations it is quite normal to find greyish brown animals similar in colouring to the brown rat and the two types may even occur in the same litter.

The black rat has been spread all over the world by man. Originally it lived in the tropical regions of the Old World. It was brought to central Europe long before the brown rat, which later became its rival and in many places supplanted it. Here and there, black and brown rats can be found living close together, but always occupying different niches. Black rats live higher up (e.g. in attics and upper storeys), brown rats at ground level. Black rats are much cleaner animals than brown rats. They like dry, warm places and live mainly on fruit and seeds. They are also less prolific than brown rats and live together much more harmoniously. The black rat can climb and jump well, but never ventures voluntarily into water. Like the brown rat, it is active mainly after dusk and during the night. In food stores (grain, fruit and other foodstuffs) it is a most unwelcome visitor.

Skull viewed from above

Brown Rat
or **Norwegian Rat**

Old World Rats and Mice
Muridae

Rattus norvegicus

The brown rat is a moderately large rodent. Its body measures 190—270 mm, its tail 130—200 mm and its hind paw 38—45 mm. The condylobasal length of its skull is 44—53 mm. Its scaly tail is practically hairless and is never longer than its body. When curved over, its ears do not reach its eyes. It has a brownish grey back and a dingy white underside.

Like the house mouse, the brown rat now lives on all the continents and most of the islands of the world — thanks to man. It is not known exactly where it originally came from, but this was probably eastern Asia, where it is still to be found in the wild. Wild brown rat populations also exist in Europe, but by far the greater majority of these animals are co-habitants of man and frequent buildings, sewers, cow-sheds, stables, pig-sties, slaughterhouses, etc.

In the open, the brown rat always lives near water, as it likes water and is a good swimmer. Indoors, it lives in cellars, under floor-boards, etc. Brown rats dig a whole maze of underground passages at a depth of up to 40 cm, with nest chambers and food stores. As a rule, they come out in search of food in the evening and at night.

Brown rats are polygamous and the females produce 2—3 litters of 6—12 young a year.

The brown rat is not persecuted only because of its gluttony. Far more serious is its habit of frequenting dirty, contaminated places and carrying the germs of dangerous infections to food stores, etc. It must therefore be combated primarily for reasons of health and hygiene.

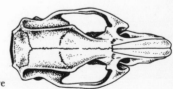

Skull viewed from above

Common Hamster

Cricetus cricetus

New World Rats and Mice
Cricetidae

The common hamster is a robust, moderately large rodent with a very brightly coloured coat. Its body measures 240—340 mm, its tail only 40—60 mm. Its hind paw is 30—40 mm long and the condylobasal length of its skull is 46—52 mm. Its most distinctive feature is its large facial pouches.

The common hamster is a solitary animal living in burrows. The main part of the burrow is a roomy dwelling chamber with a vertical entrance and a sloping exit. Another chamber acts as a store-room, which, by the end of the autumn, may contain up to 15 kg of grain, potatoes, sugar beet, etc. The dwelling chamber contains the grass-lined nest where the female gives birth to the young. Hamsters generally spend most of their life in this chamber. For a large part of the year (roughly from October to April), they hibernate deep underground, completely cut off from the outside world, as they seal their burrows before retiring. From time to time they wake and dip into their stores. In the spring, soon after they wake, the male and female copulate. The female produces 2—3 litters of 4—12 young in a year. The gestation period is 20 days. At the age of 17 days, the young start to explore the world outside.

The hamster stuffs food into its facial pouches, with contortions which look as if it was trying to swallow a difficult morsel. The pouches hold about 50 g of grain. If surprised by an enemy, the animal quickly empties them and sits up on its hind legs, snapping its teeth and spitting.

The common hamster's area of distribution extends from France, across central and eastern Europe, to the river Yenisei in Siberia. It is confined to steppes and cultivated land (fields).

Norwegian Lemming

Lemmus lemmus

Lemmings are related to voles. Of their several species, the best known in Europe is the Norwegian lemming, a typical inhabitant of the Arctic tundra. In Scandinavia it lives in treeless and wooded tundra, where forests alternate with large peat-bogs. It extends across Finland to the Kola Peninsula, where it also lives on the coast. In the south it is found in mountains. The Norwegian lemming has a yellowish brown coat with black markings. Its body measures 130—150 mm, its tail only 15—18 mm. Its short ears are hidden by its fur. In general appearance it resembles a hamster and it also has a similar nature. When attacked by an enemy, it squeaks, spits and bites and puts up a brave fight even against human beings. It hides under boulders and tree stumps and builds a network of passages in the thick carpet of peat-bogs. Its spherical nest, which is made of grass, lichen and moss, is built near the surface of the ground, e.g. under fallen trees or stones, or in moss and peat. In the spring, after the snow has melted, we can find quantities of nests built by lemmings on the ground during the winter, under the snow. Lemmings are mainly vegetarians. Twice a year (under favourable conditions three times), the female gives birth to 5—6 young. Young born in the spring themselves have young towards the end of the summer. If conditions are favourable (at intervals of 3—4 years), lemmings multiply to such an extent in some regions that they overrun the tundra and many of them are forced to migrate. They all trek en masse in the same direction, even swimming across wide rivers and throw themselves into the sea. Most of them die on the way. At the same time their enemies — foxes, stoats, owls and birds of prey — also reproduce at a higher rate.

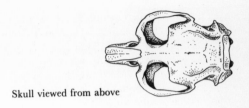

Skull viewed from above

Bank Vole

New World Rats and Mice
Cricetidae

Clethrionomys glareolus

Like the Norwegian lemming, the bank vole belongs to the voles, which differ substantially from true mice. In the first place, they are stockier, their tail and hind paws are shorter in proportion to their body, and their ears, which are also shorter, are almost hidden by their fur. Mice have large eyes, voles smallish eyes. The molars are constantly being worn down, but they grow continuously for the whole of the animal's life and have no roots. The only exceptions are the muskrat and the bank vole, in which, in old animals, they acquire roots. The bank vole's body measures 90—110 mm, its tail about half that length (40—55 mm). Its hind paw measures 14—18 mm and its skull 22—26 mm. Its coat is rusty brown, with a silvery white underside.

The bank vole is a forest-dweller, but is also content with a group of trees or a dike with a row of oaks and bushes. It is to be found both inside woods and on their outskirts, in dry places and on the banks of streams, in mountains and in lowlands. Its nest is usually situated below the surface of the ground. In the winter it ascends into the branches of young trees and gnaws the bark.

Bank voles reproduce from April to August and have 3—7 young several times a year. The young leave the nest at about three weeks and themselves start reproducing soon afterwards. The females mature very quickly and when three and a half months old may already have young of their own.

The bank vole inhabits the greater part of Europe (but not Ireland, the Iberian Peninsula, Italy and the southern Balkans), western Siberia, Asia Minor and Transcaucasia. It is one of the commonest rodents.

Upper (left) and lower (right) row of molars

Muskrat

Ondatra zibethicus

New World Rats and Mice
Cricetidae

The muskrat is the largest European vole. It is actually a native of North America, where it lives over a vast area, from Alaska to Louisiana. In 1905, five pairs of muskrats were set free beside a pond in central Bohemia. They multiplied so rapidly that they soon spread over the whole of Bohemia and from there to Germany, Austria, Poland, Switzerland, Hungary, Yugoslavia, Rumania and Bulgaria. Muskrats were also introduced in many parts of the USSR, Finland and other countries. There are no muskrats in southern Europe, however.

The muskrat has a glossy dark brown or chestnut-brown coat, with a greyish brown underside. It has a distinctive long, flat-sided tail, which it uses like a rudder when swimming. Its hind legs are used as oars and the toes are edged with special bristles, which spread out when the animal is swimming, thereby increasing the area of the foot. The muskrat's body measures 31—35 cm, its tail 20—25 cm and its hind paw 6—8 cm. A special gland near its genitals secretes a substance with a strong musky odour. It is an essentially aquatic animal.

The muskrat has two types of lair. In steep banks it digs long, horizontal burrows terminating in a nest chamber lined with dry plants. The burrow is always entered under water and here and there in the course of its passages there are ventilating shafts. Where the waterside is flat and does not allow the excavation of underground burrows, we often see, in the rushes, large structures reminiscent of beavers' lodges. The female gives birth to 7—8 young up to four times a year and those of the first litter may already have young of their own in the same year.

Hind foot

Martino's Snow Vole

New World Rats and Mice
Cricetidae

Dolomys bogdanovi

Both in appearance and, for the most part, in its mode of life, this species resembles the snow vole, but it is larger, has a relatively longer tail and its ears clearly protrude from its fur. Its coat, which is silky and comparatively long, is bluish grey to brownish grey on the back and greyish white on the underside. Its hairy tail is grey on top and white on the underside. An adult specimen measures 126—149 mm, its tail 90—110 mm, its hind paw 24—26 mm and its ear 18—20 mm. The condylobasal length of its skull is 31—35 mm.

The Martino's snow vole is excellently adapted for life among stones and boulders. Its long vibrissae (tactile whiskers), which may measure up to 6 cm, help it to feel its way in the dark. So far, the only place where this vole is known to exist is Yugoslavia, where it lives mainly in or near limestone formations. In most cases, this interesting mammal has been found at altitudes of over 1,000 m, and sometimes also not far above sea level (e.g. near Lake Skadar, or Scutari). The Martino's snow vole does not dig burrows and spends most of its life in the deep, dark spaces below boulders and in crevices in rocks. Like other voles, it can be traced by the trail of food remains it leaves behind it — bitten stalks and grass blades, leaves and roots.

The history of how it came to be identified is worth mentioning. The genus *Dolomys* had previously been known only from fossil finds. When this species was discovered in the mountains of Montenegro, in 1922, it was at first taken to be a relative of the snow vole and it was only later that it was found to be the last extant relic of the genus *Dolomys*.

Upper (left) and lower (right) row of molars

Water Vole

Arvicola terrestris

New World Rats and Mice
Cricetidae

The water vole is the largest native European vole, since the muskrat was introduced there by man. Its body measures 130—190 mm, its tail 75—125 mm and its hind paw 27—32 mm. The condylobasal length of its skull is 33—38 mm. As a rule it is dark brown, but light grey and black variants are also known.

As its name implies, the water vole lives chiefly near water and swims and dives extremely well. Its burrows, which it builds mainly in the banks of streams or beside stagnant water, run just below the surface of the ground. Their location can often be detected from the flattened mounds of earth thrown up during their construction. Water voles have underground nests, but they also often build spherical nests made from dry aquatic plants, among rushes, in the lower branches of partly submerged shrubs or on the floating nests of aquatic birds. If we break into a water vole's burrow, we usually also find stocks of food in it, including piles of bitten-off roots, twigs, tubers, etc.

Water is not the water vole's sole element, however, and we may often encounter it in gardens and in potato and sugar beet fields, especially in the autumn. As a matter of fact, it is still under debate whether there are two strains of water vole (an 'aquatic' type and a 'terrestrial' type), or only one strain, the members of which, when the nesting season is over, leave the water and seek drier quarters. The female can produce 3—4 litters of 2—8 young in a year.

During the winter, water voles like to gnaw the roots of trees. The area of distribution of the water vole covers almost the whole of Europe and extends as far as the river Lena in Siberia, the Near East and Iran. Several geographical races exist.

Upper (left) and lower (right) row of molars

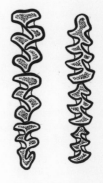

Common Vole

Microtus arvalis

New World Rats and Mice
Cricetidae

The common vole is the most abundant mammal in European fields and meadows. Its back is greyish brown or yellowish grey and its underside is greyish white or pale ochre. Its body measures 90—120 mm, its tail is relatively short (30—40 per cent of its body length) and the length of its hind paw never exceeds 18 mm. The condylobasal length of its skull varies from 22 to 27 mm.

The common vole inhabits open country in the plains and on the lower slopes of hills and mountains. It is to be found over the whole of Europe except England, Scandinavia and parts of the Mediterranean region and also lives in Kazakhstan, the southeast of central Asia and southern Siberia.

In some years, the common vole over-proliferates. It overruns fields, meadows and the outskirts of woods and riddles them with countless holes. Our knowledge of the causes of this periodic over-proliferation is at present very small, but one of them is the unique reproductive capacity of voles. In favourable circumstances, the female common vole can give birth for the first time at the age of five weeks. The female young attain sexual maturity by the age of only 30 days, while they are still being suckled. The old females mate again immediately after littering and since the gestation period is 19—21 days, they can continuously produce litters at three-week intervals.

The usual number of young in a litter is 4—12. Litters of up to 15 young have been recorded, but there is a possibility that they may have come from two females.

Voles live chiefly on the green parts of plants. Flesh forms only a very small proportion of their diet. In times of over-proliferation they do immense damage to crops.

Upper (left) and lower (right) row of molars

Short-tailed Vole

Microtus agrestis

New World Rats and Mice
Cricetidae

The coat of the short-tailed vole is dark brown and its short ears are so well hidden by its fur that their tips are only just visible. The length of its hind paw, which usually measures 18—19 mm, is another important identification mark, as it is longer than the common vole's hind paw. The short-tailed vole's body measures 95—120 mm, its tail 30—47 mm; the condylobasal length of its skull is 23—29 mm. Its most reliable differential character, however, is the shape of its second upper molar, which has an extra ring on its grinding surface.

The short-tailed vole lives beside water, in marshes, near the source of forest streams and in the vegetation growing on their banks. In the mountains, it ascends to the meadows above the tree line. Traces of its activities — small piles of bitten grass and rush stalks — can be seen beside water and on marshy ground.

Like other voles, the short-tailed vole is active both in the daytime and at night, periods of rest alternating with spells of activity at intervals of 2—4 hours. It builds relatively large nests either just below the surface of the ground or directly on the ground, in reeds and grass. The female produces up to four litters of 4—7 young in a year. The reproductive capacity of this rodent is thus not far behind that of the common vole and it displays the same tendency to local over-proliferation.

The short-tailed vole has a larger area of distribution than the common vole, as it lives further north. It inhabits the temperate and cold belt of Europe and Asia, as far as Mongolia. In central Europe, its occurrence in plains and foothills is sporadic, but in the mountains it is common everywhere. In England it occupies the niche of the common vole.

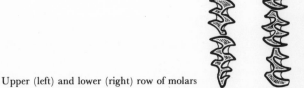

Upper (left) and lower (right) row of molars

Snow Vole

Microtus nivalis

New World Rats and Mice
Cricetidae

Like the marmot and the chamois, the snow vole is a typical representative of the fauna of high mountains. It lives on rocky slopes, in moraine and in meadows strewn with large boulders, from the upper limit of the dwarf (knee) pine belt as far as any vegetation can be found.

The snow vole's coat is an unusual silvery grey or greyish brown shade and its underside is greyish white. Its body measures 114—143 mm, its hind paw 19—21 mm and its skull 27.8—30.9 mm. Its tail, which measures about 45 per cent of its body length, is generally all one colour. Its thick, soft fur affords it much-needed protection against the rigours of the climate, while its long whiskers indicate that it lives almost entirely in dark crevices and holes.

The snow vole inhabits the Sierra de Gredos in Spain, the Pyrenees, the Alps, the Carpathians, the Balkans, Asia Minor and Lebanon and extends in the east to the Caucasus and Kopet Dagh in Turkmenistan. As a rule, it lives above the tree line and in the Alps it occurs at altitudes of up to 4,000 m, but in boulder fields in the Maritime Alps it descends to only a few hundred metres above sea level. Very often, it drags food under stones, or into burrows opening under boulders. After a gestation period of 21 days, the female gives birth to 2—7 young, which open their eyes at 13 days and are suckled for three weeks. The mountain summer is brief and so the snow vole usually has only one litter (and never more than two). It seldom digs burrows, as the mazes among the rocks offer it adequate shelter and spaces for building its nest. As a rule, it survives only one winter.

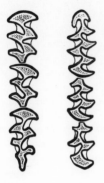

Upper (left) and lower (right) row of molars

Northern Vole

Microtus oeconomus

New World Rats and Mice
Cricetidae

The northern vole resembles the short-tailed vole. It has a dark brown back, with a darker (and sometimes almost indistinguishable) stripe down the middle. Its greyish white underside sometimes has a faint yellowish tinge. Members of the central European northern vole population have the following dimensions: body length 105 — 142 mm, tail 48 — 63 mm, hind paw 18.5 — 22.6 mm, condylobasal length of skull 26.3 — 30.5 mm. The first molar in the upper jaw is a good differential character.

The northern vole is distributed over a large part of northern Europe and Asia. It occurs mainly in the taiga and the tundra belt, where it inhabits damp places, such as dank woods, swamps and river banks. A few, isolated populations are also to be found to the south of the main northern area of distribution of this rodent. Small populations live in Holland, beside Lake Neusiedler in Austria and, in central Europe, beside Lake Balaton and in the Danube basin.

The northern vole does comparatively little digging. It builds a nest above the ground, e.g. on a tussock of reed-grass, where it is fairly safe from floods. It excavates relatively simple burrows in dikes or river banks and makes underground nests in them. Its diet consists of the crisp parts of aquatic plants and it is particularly fond of young rush shoots. It betrays its presence by its runs in the reeds, sedge and grass and by the remains of its meals, with the faeces near by.

The northern vole is a good swimmer and can also dive. In one year it produces up to four litters of 2 — 9 young. The female may give birth to its first young at the age of only six weeks.

Upper (left) and lower (right) row of molars

Northern Root Vole

Pitymys subterraneus

New World Rats and Mice
Cricetidae

The northern root vole looks like a small common vole, but if we take a close look we can see certain differences. In the first place, the northern root vole has very small eyes and short ears, hidden by its fur. Its coat is very similar to that of the common vole. It is brownish grey (sometimes greyish black), but is finer and thicker. On the sole of its hind paw there are five fleshy pads (in other voles six). Its body measures 80—106 mm. In proportion to its body length, its tail (24—32 mm) and its hind paw (14—15.5 mm) are shorter than in other voles. Its markedly flat skull measures about 22 mm.

The northern root vole's area of distribution extends from France to southern Ukraine, Asia Minor and north-western Iran, but it is not distributed evenly and in some regions it is absent altogether. In lowlands it occurs in isolated islands, but it is a common animal in the mountains, where it always lives in shady spots with a thick layer of humus, giving it plenty of scope for its burrowing activities. At low altitudes we are also more likely to find it in loose soil, in compost heaps, in fields, meadows and gardens. Wherever it can, it riddles the whole area with its shallow burrows, which often simply raise the soil a little and here and there open on to the surface.

The northern root vole is less prolific than other voles, as it has only 2—3 young in a litter. Nevertheless, it over-proliferates in mountainous regions in some years. Like other voles, it has a life span of about eighteen months. It is entirely herbivorous and lives mainly on the green parts of plants.

Upper (left) and lower (right) row of molars

Tatra Vole

Pitymys tatricus

The Tatra vole is a close relative of the northern root vole. It occurs only in the High and Low Tatras in Slovakia, at altitudes of 1,400 to 2,300 m, and was first discovered in 1952. This new and interesting species attracted considerable attention among zoologists. At first, it seemed to be related to races of voles in the Balkan Mountains, the Alps and the mountains of central Asia, but a detailed study showed that it was a completely separate, independent species.

In general appearance the Tatra vole resembles the common vole. It is larger than the northern root vole and its colouring varies from grey-brown ochre to yellowish cinnamon brown with a rusty tinge. Its underside is greyish white. Its small eyes show that it belongs to the genus *Pitymys*. The Tatra vole's body measures 90—120 mm, its tail 31—46 mm, its hind paw (which is relatively longer than that of the northern root vole) 16.5 to 18.5 mm and its skull 22.7—25 mm.

The Tatra vole inhabits the upper part of the forest belt, the dwarf (knee) pine zone and the meadows above the tree line. The exits from its burrows often lie under rocks. Near the upper margin of mountain forests it also lives under rotting trunks and tree stumps, in similar places to the northern root vole. It likewise has only 2—3 young in a litter, but the female produces only four litters in a year, while the northern root vole may have five. Female burrowing voles can also have young during their first year, but female Tatra voles do not mature and have young until the next calendar year. This is evidently the outcome of adaptation to the hardships of life in the mountains, where the harsh climatic conditions greatly reduce the length of the reproductive period.

Crested Porcupine

Hystrix cristata

The only parts of Europe where this large rodent occurs are Sicily and the south of Italy. Claims that it also lived in Greece were unfounded. The main area of distribution of the crested porcupine is North and North-west Africa. Since the porcupines living in Italy do not form a separate geographical race, most zoologists assume that this animal was brought there by the Romans.

The crested porcupine is a large rodent with a short, blunt snout and weighing 10—15 kg. Its body measures 57—70 cm, its tail 5—12 cm. Its head, neck, shoulders and abdomen are covered with bristles, while the rest of its body is armed with hard, black- and white-striped, hollow spines. The spines on the tail are open, like tubes. The length of the spines is 30—40 cm.

This solitary, nocturnal animal hides by day in natural hollows or in burrows, which it sometimes digs itself. During the cold part of the year, it may stay 'indoors' for several days at a time. It lives in dry, flat country or at the foot of mountains, on rugged ground with sufficient shelter. Its varied diet includes roots, tubers, different fruits and berries (e.g. figs, grapes and dates) and small animals. Like most rodents, it can hold its food in its fore paws. In the mating season the males and females live in pairs. After a gestation period of about eight weeks, the female gives birth in a burrow to 2—4 young, whose spines are at first short and soft, and which soon start to accompany their mother out of the burrow. Porcupines can live for up to 15 years.

When alarmed, the crested porcupine rattles its spines and tail, stamps on the ground and growls.

European Wild Cat

Felis silvestris

Europe has two wild species of cats — the lynx and the smaller wild cat, which closely resembles the gentler domestic tabby in appearance. It is more powerfully built than the domestic cat, however, has relatively shorter legs, a wider head and a vertical, instead of sloping, forehead. Its short, thick, bushy tail is marked with dark stripes and the tip looks as if it had been lopped off. The colouring of the European wild cat is very variable. The basic colour of its coat is grey or yellowish grey and it is vividly striped, especially on the back and legs. Its size is likewise very variable. Its body measures 50—80 cm, its tail 25—40 cm, its hind paw 12—13 cm and its skull 8—10.3 cm. Of its 30 teeth, the longest are the canines. An adult wild cat stands 35—40 cm at the shoulder and its weight varies from 3 to 11 kg.

The European wild cat inhabits Europe, Asia and Africa and its various geographical races are very different from each other. The common wild cat has already been wiped out in many parts of Europe. The only places where it has managed to survive are a number of mountainous regions, including the Carpathians, where there is still a comparatively flourishing population.

Voles and mice account for two thirds of the wild cat's diet. Otherwise it eats small birds and lizards. Probably the only time when it ventures to attack larger prey, such as hares or deer, is while it is feeding its young. Wild cats mate in February and March. Once a year, after a gestation period of 63 days, the female gives birth to 3—4 young in a warm lair in a hollow tree, a cleft in a rock, a deserted fox's den or a badger's sett. The kittens, which are blind at birth, open their eyes at the age of 9—11 days.

168

Footprints of a lynx (left) and a cat (right)

European Lynx

Lynx lynx

The European wild cat, and all small cats in general, have elongated, slit-like pupils, but the lynx and other large cats have round pupils. The lynx is a large, robust beast of prey distinguished by tufted ears and bushy whiskers, a short, 'lopped-off' tail and long, strong legs. Its greyish yellow or light russet back is marked with dark spots.

Its body measures 70—140 cm, its tail 15—31 cm and its hind paw 19—22 cm. The condylobasal length of its skull is 12—15 cm, it stands 60—75 cm at the shoulder and can weigh up to 40 kg.

The lynx is a native of Europe, Asia and America, but was exterminated long ago in western Europe. It inhabits dense forests with rocks and the average area of its preserve is several square kilometres. To demarcate its domain it uses urine and faeces (which it does not bury like the wild cat) and scratches on the bark of trees.

When hunting, the lynx relies primarily on its hearing and vision. Usually, it sits on a high perch, keeping a look-out, and then either drops on to its prey's back, or bounds after it. Neither roe deer, nor small or weak red deer are safe from the lynx, but for the most part it lives on small rodents and birds.

The mating period lasts from January to March. During this time the males' calls can be heard far and wide and they often fight with each other. After a gestation period of 9—10 weeks, the female gives birth to 2—4 young in a fissure in the rocks, between the roots of trees, in a deserted fox's den or in a badger's sett. The young are suckled for five months, but are already capable of catching small prey at the age of 40 days.

European Genet

Genetta genetta

The European genet is a typical representative of the oldest beasts of prey, the weasel cats, which have 40 teeth (far more than true cats). They are small animals with short legs and a long body and resembling a weasel or a marten in appearance. The European genet has a yellow coat, with vague rows of black spots running the length of its body, and a long, black-ringed tail, which is very wide at the base. Its body measures 47—58 cm, its tail 41—48 cm and its hind paw 7.5—8.5 cm. Its claws are partly retractile.

The European genet is very retiring and prefers country with rugged rocks or boulders and plenty of shrubs. With its lithe, sinuous body it can slip through the smallest cracks and can climb trees with great agility. If alarmed, it dashes for shelter, but if cornered, it utters loud screeches, swishes its tail and releases a malodorous secretion from a special abdominal gland. As a rule, it stays well out of sight during the daytime, but after dusk it comes out of hiding and spends the whole night hunting prey.

Mating occurs in February and March. In April or May the female gives birth to 2—3 young in a simple lair between the roots of trees, in a bush or in a crevice in the rocks. The genet does not build burrows. It catches birds, small rodents and lizards and sucks birds' eggs. Rats are its favourite prey, however, and it will pursue them right up to human habitations, making the most of the opportunity to raid hen-houses and dove-cotes at the same time.

The European genet also lives in Africa, but its main area of distribution is across the Iberian Peninsula to the south of France. It is rarely seen west of the Rhône and the Loire.

Wolf

Canis lupus

The wolf is a typical representative of the canine beasts of prey, all of which have a large number of teeth (usually 42). Their senses of smell and hearing are keener than their vision.

The wolf's coat is greyish brown or greyish yellow and is always darker on the back than on the underside. The wolf's body measures 100—130 cm, its tail 30—50 cm, its hind paw 25—31 cm and its skull 20.7—26.2 cm. Its weight varies from 30 to 60 kg and a powerful male may weigh as much as 70 kg. The wolf inhabits large regions in Europe, Asia and North America. It has been wiped out in many parts of Europe and today we can find it there only in the north and the east, Spain, Italy and the Balkans. In recent years wolves have been seen in East and West Germany and western Czechoslovakia. Wolves are exceedingly wary and shy animals.

For most of their lives, wolves live in families or packs. They do not go hunting until after sundown. The pack may run 40 to 80 km in the course of a night, but the wolves never go beyond the bounds of their own preserve.

As a beast of prey, the wolf is extremely bold and will tackle anything from a mouse or a vole to an elk or domestic cattle. Large animals are naturally attacked only by packs.

The mating period, which lasts about two weeks, falls in the winter and during it the wolves can be heard howling. When the couples have paired off, they separate from the pack and live a solitary existence for a time. After 63—65 days, the female gives birth to 4—6 (occasionally up to 9) young in a lair or a burrow. The young are at first unable to see and the female looks after them for a long time, and the male keeps her supplied with food.

Footprints of a wolf (left) and a dog (right)

Indian Jackal

Canine Beasts of Prey
Canidae

Canis aureus

The Indian jackal resembles a small wolf in appearance, but its colouring is redder and its ears are somewhat shorter. Its body measures 80—105 cm, its tail 20—24 cm and its skull not more than 19 cm. An adult specimen weighs 10—15 kg.

It inhabits open country (steppes, grasslands) and in the mountains is not found at altitudes of over 1,000 m. It is active in the evening and at night. During the daytime it hides in thickets or dense reed-beds and it particularly likes to be near water. The jackal has a very varied diet. It eats carcasses, catches small vertebrates (e.g. lizards, small and larger mammals and poultry), collects birds' eggs and, as an analysis of the contents of its stomach shows, also eats plant food. It is very unpopular with hunters because of the appreciable damage it sometimes does to game.

After a gestation period of about 60 days, the female gives birth to the young, usually in a natural hollow in rocks, between the roots of trees or in a deserted fox's den or badger's sett. If none of these is available, it digs a burrow of its own. In regions where they live, jackals can be identified by their frequent howling. The Indian jackal still abounds in central and southern Asia, in Asia Minor and in North Africa. The only places where it is still found in Europe are the Balkans and occasionally Hungary. It ought to be protected by law in Europe, as its population there is rapidly diminishing.

Footprint

Fox

Vulpes vulpes

Canine Beasts of Prey
Canidae

The fox is the most abundant canine beast of prey in Europe. It occurs in several colour varieties, most commonly with red coat, white throat and underside, and black legs, but the inner surface of its ears is always black and the tip of its tail is white. The body of an adult fox measures 70—80 cm, its bushy tail 34—45 cm, its hind paw 14—16 cm and its skull 12.8—16 cm. It weighs 4—12 kg.

The fox is a cautious and retiring animal with a very keen sense of smell, hearing and vision. As a rule, it goes hunting only in the evening or early morning. It lives mainly in woods with rocks and ravines, where it generally chooses dry places.

Foxes build deep burrows and as they sometimes live in them for many years, in time they become complicated underground structures with numerous entrances and exits. It hunts within a radius of 6—8 km, marking the limits of its domain with faeces 'labelled' with material secreted by its scent glands. In addition, foxes have another scent gland above the base of their tail, which is a further source of their specific 'foxy' odour.

Foxes mate in January and February and the couples remain together until the young are independent. Soon after mating, the female gives the whole lair a thick lining of soft hair plucked from its own abdomen. After 52—54 days it gives birth to 3—8 blind young, which open their eyes at the age of 14 or 15 days. When the young are able to start taking flesh, the parents keep them supplied with hares, pheasants, chickens, ducks, etc., but for the rest of the year the fox makes itself useful by catching small rodents. About 20 per cent of its diet consists of greenstuff.

The fox is distributed over the whole of Europe, Asia, North Africa and North America.

Footprint

Arctic Fox

Alopex lagopus

Together with the polar bear, the arctic fox lives further north than other mammals. It inhabits the woodless lowland and mountain tundras of the far north. In Europe, it occurs on the islands of the Arctic Ocean and in the tundras of Scandinavia and the USSR.

The arctic fox is smaller than the red fox. Its tail is all one colour and its rounded ears only just peep out of its fur. Its body measures 60—70 cm and its tail 28—33 cm. In the summer, arctic foxes have a brownish grey back and a greyish white underside, but in the winter they turn pure white. Their winter coat is very soft and thick and is greatly coveted by furriers. The silver fox is a rare colour variant of the arctic fox. It forms 4—5 per cent of the population and its winter coat is greyish blue. Living where it does, the arctic fox cannot afford to be fussy over its food. It subsists chiefly on rodents and the size of its population depends largely on the supply of Norwegian lemmings. It catches birds and raids their nests, but is not above eating carrion thrown up on the shore by the sea, and is also partial to the fatty dung of polar bears. In times of plenty, it lays in stocks of food, burying them in the snow. It lives in small communities and hunts both by day and by night. Mating occurs in March or April. During this period the foxes are very noisy and their barking and howling can be heard all over the tundra. Skirmishes also take place occasionally between the males. The lair in which the 10—15 young are reared is in a burrow dug by the fox in a carefully chosen spot. If unable to dig a burrow, it makes its lair in a crevice in the rocks, or between blocks of ice.

Pine Marten

Martes martes

Mustelids
Mustelidae

We have chosen the pine marten as the first representative of the mustelids, moderately large, weasel-like beasts of prey with relatively short legs, soft, thick fur and 28—32 teeth.

It can be distinguished from the beech marten by the plain, honey-coloured spot on its throat. Its paws, which have hairs even on the sole pads, are another good identification mark. The short hairs in its coat are yellowish. Its erect ears have a light-coloured margin and its nose is black. The pine marten's body measures 38—58 cm, its tail 22—28 cm, its hind paw 8—11 cm and its skull 8—8.8 cm. It weighs 1—1.4 kg.

The pine marten inhabits wooded regions over the whole of Europe and a large part of Asia. It is a solitary animal. During the daytime it shelters in hollow trees or the nests of squirrels and birds of prey and does its hunting in the evening or morning. It can climb trees very nimbly and, if necessary, can leap from one tree to another, for distances of up to 3.5 metres. It has excellent vision and hearing.

The mating season lasts from the end of July to the end of August. Before starting to develop, the fertilized ova 'rest' for a time in the female's body, so that the young are not born until the following April, after 245—289 days. The young have a very soft coat. They are blind at birth and do not open their eyes for 24—38 days, but at the age of two months they leave the nest. Martens attain sexual maturity at two years and have a life span of 8—10 years.

The pine marten lives chiefly on small vertebrates (voles, mice and birds, but particularly squirrels).

It inhabits Europe as far as the Caucasus; western Asia as far as the rivers Ob and Irtysh; Asia Minor and Iran.

Haired paw

Beech Marten

Martes foina

The beech marten originally lived in hollows and fissures in rocks. Today, however, we are probably more likely to encounter it near human communities, and in lieu of rocks it has actually been known to settle in old buildings in towns. It seeks shelter in piles of stones, in old masonry or in attics, sheds, etc. It inhabits Europe (as far as the Baltic in the north) and Asia as far as northern China.

The beech marten is roughly the same size as the pine marten, but its coat is more a greyish brown shade and the short hairs are white. There are no hairs on its sole pads. The spot on its throat is white and forks down to its limbs, while its nose is light and flesh-coloured.

It reproduces in the same way as the pine marten, except that the gestation period is slightly shorter ($8\frac{1}{2}$ months). The embryo stops developing for a time, just as in the case of the pine marten.

The beech marten climbs trees with great agility, but hunts mainly on the ground. Various small mammal pests are the chief component of its diet and an analysis of the contents of the stomachs of martens caught near human communities showed that rats formed 80 per cent of their food. Unfortunately, they also attack wild birds and poultry. Occasionally they wreak havoc in henhouses, because if they get into one containing a large number of birds, they may bite all of them in a fit of panic. They do not suck their blood, however, as some people suppose. Like the pine marten, the beech marten is fond of fruit and eggs.

Not many people are acquainted with the beech marten's growling, barking voice, which is heard chiefly during the mating season.

Haired paw

Stoat

Mustela erminea

As distinct from the weasel, which only sometimes develops a white coat in winter, the stoat always has a white winter coat, but whether it is wearing its summer coat, which is brown except for the white underside, or its snow-white winter coat, it can always be recognized from its black-tipped tail.

The stoat is larger than the weasel. Its body measures 24—29 cm, its tail 8—9 cm, its hind paw 3.7—4.4 cm and its skull 4.1—5.1 cm. The male is always larger than the female.

Like the weasel, the stoat is lithe and nimble and can easily slip through narrow spaces. It also lives in similar places to the weasel, but does not avoid damp spots and occurs high up in the mountains. It swims quite well and can run at roughly the same speed as a human being.

The stoat is a sworn foe of harmful rodents and the size of its population depends on the supply of these pests. It only consumes about 65 g of food daily, while its own body weight is 150—350 g.

If stoats mate in the spring (February to March), the subsequent gestation period is two months. If they mate in the summer, it is eight months, as the ovum remains quiescent for a long time before developing. Once a year the female gives birth to 4—8 blind young, which open their eyes after about 40 days. The nest lies in a space between stones, in old masonry or in a hole in the ground.

The stoat marks out its territory with faeces. In the event of danger, it releases from its anal gland a malodorous secretion to frighten the enemy away.

The stoat inhabits central and northern Europe, northern and central Asia as far as Japan, and North America.

Weasel

Mustela nivalis

Mustelids
Mustelidae

The weasel is a small beast of prey with a sinuous body and short legs, a brown back and a white underside. The weasel's winter coat is somewhat lighter. Its tail is the same colour as its back and does not have a black tip like the stoat's tail.

The weasel's size is very variable, differences between the males and females being particularly marked. The male's body measures 17.3—25.8 cm, the female's 15.9—19.1 cm. The male's tail is 5—8 cm long, the female's 4—5.5 cm, while the length of their hind paws is 2.4—3.8 and 2.1—2.6 cm respectively. A similar pronounced sex-linked difference is to be found in the length of the skull, which measures 3.5—4.4 cm in males and 3—3.5 cm in females.

The weasel inhabits open country and its favourite haunts are piles of stones, rubble, demolished bridges, etc. It is rarely encountered deep in the forest, avoids damp places and usually gives human communities a wide berth.

There are still many gaps in our knowledge of the biology of this mammal. It does not seem to have a fixed mating time, since we can find young during the greater part of the year. The gestation period is about five weeks and the litter contains 4—7 young (seldom more). The young are born blind and open their eyes at about 25 days. The male appears to assist in the rearing of the young.

The weasel is a dreaded foe of voles and mice. It lives in Europe, North Africa and Asia as far as Japan. One variety inhabits North America. Among weasels of normal size, a strikingly small form can be found over the whole of this animal's area of distribution.

Footprints

European Polecat

Putorius putorius

The European polecat is midway between a marten and a weasel in size. Its colouring is so conspicuous that it cannot be mistaken for any other animal. It weighs about 1 kg, its body measures 33—44 cm, its tail 10—18 cm, its hind paw 6.1—6.5 cm and its skull 5.5—7.2 cm.

This mustelid is not a forest-dweller. It lives in fields and scrub and on the outskirts of woods and it often settles in the vicinity of human communities. Most of all, however, it likes to be near water. It swims well, can dive and is an expert at catching frogs and fish. It hunts its prey mainly at night. No small mammal or bird is safe when it is about and it will even attack rabbits, pheasants and poultry. A pile of stones or branches, a shed, a barn or a burrow (which it digs itself) are all it needs for shelter.

Once a year, after a gestation period of 41—42 days, the female gives birth to 3—7 blind young which open their eyes at the age of 30—36 days, after they have started taking solids. By five months the young are independent.

The European polecat inhabits Europe and western Asia and in some places (e.g. the Alps) it occurs at altitudes of up to 2,000 m.

One of the things for which the polecat is noted is its fetid smell. Like all mustelids, it has a well developed scent gland below the base of its tail. The substance secreted by this gland is used both for marking out its territory and as a defence weapon. When alarmed, the animal suddenly empties the gland of its contents, which contaminate the surrounding area to such an extent that a would-be attacker decides that discretion is the better part of valour and beats a hasty retreat.

Skull viewed from above

Asiatic Polecat

Putorius eversmanni

Unlike the European polecat, the Asiatic polecat is a light-coloured animal living in fields and steppes. The area of its distribution largely coincides with the area inhabited by the ground squirrel, telling us that the polecat lives mainly on these rodents — although it by no means despises other mammals, birds, snakes and amphibians. It inhabits deep burrows in the middle of fields lying in plains. Its slim body enables it to enter the burrows of ground squirrels, where it strikes terror into the hearts of their inhabitants, like a weasel among voles. The most westerly point that the Asiatic polecat is found is the plains of western Bohemia. From here, its area of distribution stretches east across the steppe belt to southern Siberia, Mongolia and China.

This animal has a lighter coloured coat than the European polecat and its back is sandy yellow. It has brown rings round its eyes and its underside and limbs are usually dark brown. Its tail is light near the base and dark brown towards the tip. The Asiatic polecat's body measures 29—52 cm, its tail 7—18 cm and its skull 5.2—7.1 cm. Asiatic polecats mate in March or April and the female, after 36—40 days, gives birth to 8—11 young.

It is a popular belief that all polecats are thieves and that they should be destroyed as vermin. Not even the European polecat merits its bad reputation, however, while the Asiatic polecat ought actually to be treated with respect, as a useful animal. Despite this, it is still mercilessly persecuted.

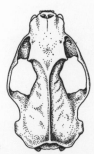

Skull viewed from above

European Mink

Lutreola lutreola

Mustelids
Mustelidae

The European mink is similar in build to a polecat. Its dark brown coat is relieved by a white spot on its chin and upper lip. Its body measures 30—40 cm and its tail 12—19 cm. Its fur is short and thick and it has well developed webbing between its toes, especially on its hind feet. The condylobasal length of its skull is 5.8—6.4 cm.

It occurs near streams and torrents, beside stagnant water and in swamps. Apart from its webbed feet, it is not specifically equipped for an aquatic mode of life, although it can dive quite well. In general appearance it resembles a polecat rather than an otter. Its diet includes invertebrate animals, but it seems to live mainly on fish, frogs and small mammals, some of which it catches under water. Like the polecat, the European mink is a bold and daring animal and will sometimes attack ducks, chickens and geese.

The European mink once lived in parts of central and western Europe with suitable conditions, as far as the south-west of France. It disappeared from central Europe, however, probably as a result of migration and a natural tendency for its numbers to diminish, rather than of intervention by man. Further east (towards the Urals and the river Irtysh), the European mink is less rare and there are still a few animals left in France. Occasional reports of an incidence of wild minks in other places were found actually to concern the American mink *(Lutreola vison)*, which is not hard to distinguish from the European species, as it has a white spot on its lower lip only. American minks are valuable for their fur and in Europe they are bred on farms, but from time to time they escape and revert to the wild state.

194

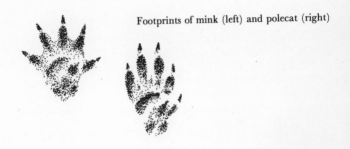

Footprints of mink (left) and polecat (right)

Wolverine or Glutton

Gulo gulo

The wolverine is the largest of the mustelids. Its body measures 70.—82.5 cm and its tail 12—15 cm. It has a short-haired, dark brown coat, a greyish white bar on its forehead and light markings on the sides of its rump. It weighs up to 30 kg. Its home is in the taigas and wooded tundras of Europe, Asia and North America. In Europe, it occurs in the most north-easterly parts, its furthest limit being the mountains of Scandinavia. Nowhere it is very abundant, however.

The wolverine is a solitary animal. It hunts its prey during the daytime and the night (in the summer mainly at night). Despite its ungainly appearance, it is very agile and is an expert hunter. It can run, climb and swim extremely well. Various arctic rodents, especially lemmings, form its staple diet, but it also eats birds, fish, frogs, carrion and fruit and berries and can overpower animals larger than itself, such as elk and reindeer calves. Its habit of sneaking unobserved into homes and stealing provisions and small livestock make it very unpopular with the human population.

The wolverine's mating period is July and August. After a gestation period of 8—9 months, the female gives birth to 1—4 young, which are unable to see for a long time and are suckled up to nine weeks. The lair is generally situated somewhere between boulders or in a cleft in a rock. When the young leave the mother, they still stay together for a time and they sometimes also hunt together. They attain adulthood at 3 years. Wolverines do not hibernate. They are persecuted more for the damage they do to game and for their thieving propensities than for their fur, which is not of great value.

Footprints

Marbled Polecat

Vormela peregusna

This slender, vividly marked little mustelid occurs in south-eastern Europe. It lives in the Ukraine, Bulgaria, Rumania and Yugoslavia and extends east across Asia Minor and central Asia to Mongolia and northern China. In the mountains of central Asia and Yugoslavia it occurs at altitudes of up to 2,000 m and more. Although it is a typical inhabitant of steppes and semi-desert country, it likes to live near water.

The ground colour of its coat is blackish brown, but its back is marked with a conspicuous pattern of yellowish white lines and spots. The distribution of the spots is very variable. Its body measures 31—38 cm, its tail 15—21 cm and its hind paw 3.5—4.5 cm. The condylobasal length of the male's skull is 5.2—5.7 cm.

The marbled polecat lives in burrows which it digs itself, or in the burrows of other mammals. It usually goes in search of prey in the morning and evening. It slinks along on its short legs looking chiefly for small rodents, but it also catches birds, reptiles and amphibians.

At present, our knowledge of this species is very limited. According to Soviet biologists, it mates in the autumn, in August and September, and the 4—8 young are born in the burrow after a long latent pregnancy. When in danger, the marbled polecat utters curious whining noises, grinds its teeth, arches its back, folds its tail over its back and squirts a malodorous substance from its anal gland.

The marbled polecat population in Europe, and in most of the rest of its area of distribution, is fast diminishing, evidently as a result of the spread of its greatest competitor for prey — the Asiatic polecat.

Skull viewed from above

Otter

Lutra lutra

Mustelids
Mustelidae

The otter is wonderfully equipped for an aquatic existence. It has a long, almost serpentine body, a flat-topped head and short ears which scarcely protrude beyond its short, thick coat. The five digits on its short, strong legs are connected by webbing.

The otter's thick brown coat is very valuable as fur. Old specimens can be recognized from their whitish neck. The otter's body measures 65—100 cm, its tail up to 50 cm, its hind paw 11—13.5 cm and its skull 8.5—12.4 cm.

Most of the otter's life is spent in or beside water and the only time when it ventures any distance away from this element is at mating time. It particularly likes clean, unregulated water and is also to be found on the coast and in river deltas. Its den is built in high, steep banks, but the burrow leading to it is always entered under water. The passage slopes upwards, so that the dwelling chamber lies above water level.

The otter does not have a fixed mating season and its young can be found at all times of the year. The gestation period is 61—63 days. In cases of latent pregnancy, when development of the embryo stops for a time, it is 9—10 months. The greatest number of young appear between April and July. The female usually gives birth in its underground den and there are generally 2—4 young in a litter. They open their eyes after about 30 days and are not fully grown until they are two years old.

The otter lives mainly on fish, which it catches under water, but it also eats frogs, small mammals and birds.

Its area of distribution covers Europe, Asia, Sumatra, Java and North Africa.

Footprints

Badger

Meles meles

Mustelids
Mustelidae

The badger has a robust body and short legs. Its body measures 60—85 cm, its relatively short tail 15—19 cm, its hind foot 10—11 cm and its skull 11.4—13.7 cm. It has 38 teeth and weighs 10—20 kg. It is a plantigrade animal, i.e. when walking it treads on the whole of its sole and not, like many other animals, on its toes (digitigrade). On either side of its white head the badger has a broad black band stretching from its nose and across its eyes to behind its ears. Its back is yellowish grey or silvery grey and its underside is black. Its fore feet are armed with long, strong claws, which are largely a burrowing implement. The badger usually digs its sett in raised ground, e.g. hills, slopes, stony spots. The sett consists of a maze of long passages with several exits. In the centre there is a roomy chamber, where the badger sleeps in the daytime, hibernates in a warmly lined bed during the winter and rears its young in the summer. The badger is not a true hibernator, however, as it wakes several times during the winter.

In June and July (the badger's mating season), we can hear its curious screeching call in the woods. After a latent pregnancy lasting 7—8 months, the 3—5 young are born between February and April. They grow very slowly and open their eyes after 28—35 days. They take their first solid food in their tenth week, but are suckled up to the age of 16 weeks.

The badger lives on earthworms, slugs and small mammals (chiefly voles and mice), which it digs out of their holes. In addition, it eats carrion, eggs, berries, seeds, roots and mushrooms. It is active mainly at night.

The badger inhabits Europe and temperate parts of Asia as far as Japan. Occasionally it is found high up in the mountains.

202

Footprint

Brown Bear

Ursus arctos

After the polar bear, the brown bear is the largest European beast of prey. Before starting to hibernate, east European bears may weigh 300 kg and sometimes more. Their body measures 150—250 cm. In general, the males are larger than the females and the same applies to the length of their skull, which measures 26.1—41.8 cm in the males and 25.7—37.3 cm in the females. The brown bear is a plantigrade animal and its large feet, which all have five toes, have flat, hairless soles.

The brown bear lives in old forests with almost inaccessible ravines, rocky ledges and slopes. It is a solitary animal and its preserve covers several square kilometres. Its lair is usually situated under an uprooted tree, in a fissure in a rock or in some similar semi-hollow place. As a rule, it does not leave its den until after dusk. When it first wakes in the spring, it lives mainly on vegetation. When the snow melts, it combs the mountains for dead game. Later in the spring it occasionally catches young animals and birds, but in the autumn it largely reverts to vegetarianism and lives chiefly on berries.

The brown bear often rouses from its winter sleep and its body temperature is maintained at the normal level. During the winter period the female gives birth to 2—5 very small, blind, helpless young. Mother and young do not emerge for another four months. The brown bear's mating season is in April and May, but the fertilized ovum does not start to develop until the end of the summer, so that the gestation period lasts 8—9 months.

The only parts of Europe where the brown bear is still to be found are the mountains (the Pyrenees, Apennines, Alps, Carpathians and Balkans) and the north. It also lives in Asia (mainly Siberia and mountainous regions) and North America.

Footprints

Polar Bear

Thalarctos maritimus

Although the number of wild specimens is today very small, almost everybody is familiar with the polar bear from visits to zoological gardens. At one time it was widely distributed over the whole of northern Europe, Asia and America and the Arctic Ocean, but its population was decimated by senseless killing. In Europe it appears only occasionally on the most northerly shores of Scandinavia, on Iceland and (more frequently) on Spitzbergen. Its coat is smooth and thick. The male, which is considerably larger than the female, measures 200—275 cm, the female not more than 185 cm. Its mean weight is about 400 kg.

The polar bear is restricted to the sea, but it cannot be regarded as an aquatic animal. It occurs on islands, on ice floes, within the limits of the ice cap and on narrow strips of continental mainland. The furthest it ever roams inland is 1—2 km. On the other hand, it is often found 20 km out at sea. It is an enduring, though not very expert or fast swimmer, as it covers only about 4—5 km in an hour. It dives, but not to any great depth, and can remain under water for about 2 minutes. Most of its time is spent hunting seals, which are its main food. Young seals, which live in special hollows under the snow for the first days after birth, are its commonest victims, but it also lies in wait for adult animals beside their air holes in the ice. In addition, the polar bear eats fish and marine birds and in the summer it supplements its menu with berries growing in the tundra. Its mating season lasts from March to June. After a gestation period of 7—8 months the female gives birth, in the middle of the winter, to 1—2 young about the same size as a rat, in a lair dug in a snowdrift on the shore.

Wild Boar

Sus scrofa

The only non-ruminant among the several wild even-toed ungulates living in Europe is the wild boar.

The wild boar's barrel-shaped body is covered with tough bristles and its long head terminates in a large, tapering snout. Its dentition shows it to be an omnivorous animal. It has a total of 44 teeth and its canines (tusks), which have an open root, grow continuously. Old males have particularly large tusks protruding upwards from both jaws. The wild boars living in western and southern Europe are considerably smaller than those of eastern Europe. Carpathian wild boars include some of the most powerful individuals. Adult, fully grown animals normally weigh 150—200 kg, but specimens weighing over 300 kg are not unknown. An adult wild boar's body measures 150—185 cm, its tail 17—26 cm, its hind foot about 25 cm and its shoulder height is 85—100 cm. The females are always smaller than the males.

The wild boar is a forest-dweller. It leaves its shelter in the thicket after dusk and hunts busily the whole night through, guided chiefly by its sense of smell and hearing. The whole year boars keep together in herds; only old individuals live solitarily. One of their favourite occupations is 'soiling' (rolling in mud or marshy ground), to cool themselves and rid themselves of parasites.

They collect acorns, beechnuts and field crops and root in the mould on the forest floor in search of roots, insect larvae and the burrows of small rodents.

Wild boars mate chiefly between November and January. After 16—20 weeks the female gives birth to 3—12 vividly striped young.

Various geographical races of the wild boar live in Europe (except England), Asia, Sumatra, Java and North Africa.

Footprint

Red Deer

Cervus elaphus

The red deer is an even-toed ungulate belonging to the same family as the fallow deer, the roe deer, the reindeer and the elk. Male deer (in the case of the reindeer both sexes) wear antlers, which are shed at a given time of year and grow again. They have a maximum life span of 25 years.

There are several races of red deer, living in North Africa, Europe, Asia and North America. In Europe, those living in the west are smaller and slighter and have a shorter face. The males weigh 150—170 kg. The Carpathian type is more robustly built, the animals have a longer face and the males weigh 200—250 kg. Their antlers are larger and develop more quickly, so that comparatively young specimens may have 6—8 tines.

The original home of the red deer was the wooded steppes, but when man started to till the ground and alter its character, the red deer took to the forests. It now visits fields and meadows only to graze.

If pursued, the red deer can develop a speed of up to 60 km per hour on even ground, but it is not a very enduring runner. It has no fear of water and will swim across turbulent rivers.

Red deer normally live in herds, but old males live solitarily. The herd is usually led by an old, experienced hind. At rutting (mating) time, however, the herd breaks up. The strongest harts each collect a group of hinds, announce possession of their territory in a trumpeting voice and warn would-be trespassers to keep away. Duels between the harts are common in the rutting season. In central Europe, the red deer's rutting season lasts from the end of September to the middle of October. After a gestation period of 34 weeks, the hind gives birth to 1 (occasionally 2) young, which she tends and suckles for a whole year.

Footprints

Axis Deer

Axis axis

Deer
Cervidae

Like the sika and the Virginian deer, the axis deer is not a native of Europe, but was brought there from the park-like woods and jungles of India and Sri Lanka. Since the middle of the 18th century, however, it has become popular in several European countries, as an attractive ornament of estates and large parks. It is now thoroughly acclimatized in England, Germany, Austria, Czechoslovakia, Yugoslavia and other countries. Sometimes it escapes from captivity and in that case may be found living wild. The axis deer has also been introduced into Australia, New Zealand, the Hawaiian Islands, Brazil and Argentina.

The axis deer has a light reddish brown coat irregularly sprinkled with white spots, except for the last row on its sides, where they form a kind of stripe. Down the middle of its back it has a black stripe. Its head and neck are relatively short. The male's antlers are far less richly branched than those of the red deer and an adult animal usually has only five tines (occasionally seven). The axis deer's body measures 130—150 cm, its tail (which is relatively long for a deer) 20—30 cm and it stands 85—95 cm at the shoulder. It weighs 75—100 kg. Interdigital glands are present on its hind feet only. Its life span is about 12 years.

Since the axis deer comes from a warm part of the world, it does not have a regular rutting season. The female gives birth to 1—2 young — under favourable conditions at intervals of 6 months. The males shed their antlers irregularly, at different times of the year.

Captive axis deer lose their fear of man. They are particularly aggressive at rutting time and sometimes they may even be dangerous.

212

Fallow Deer

Dama dama

The fallow deer originally lived round the north-eastern corner of the Mediterranean, but was brought to western Europe many centuries ago; it has flourished in central Europe since the Middle Ages.

It is smaller than the red deer. The male weighs 60—100 kg, the female 30—60 kg. Its body measures 130—150 cm, its tail 16—19 cm. In the summer, its coat is reddish brown, with large numbers of white spots, and has a dark stripe down the middle of the back. Its winter coat is cinnamon brown and the white spots are less distinct. Round its anus they merge to form a white, black-ringed patch. The fallow deer has a black tail, which is longer than that of the red deer. The adult male has palmated antlers. The fallow deer is a typical lowland animal. It likes deciduous and mixed woods.

Fallow deer live in herds and seem to be diurnal rather than nocturnal animals. They have keener vision than the red deer, but their sense of smell and hearing are about the same. Their antlers, which finish growing in September, are not shed until the following May. As a rule, the rutting season falls in November.

The gestation period is 7½ months and the female gives birth to 1 or (quite frequently) 2 young.

The fallow deer lives on the same type of diet as the red deer. In the winter, when its normal food is covered with a thick blanket of snow, it bites off the buds of bushes and trees and nibbles the bark. It does less damage than the red deer in the woods, but it is not a welcome guest in the fields.

The fallow deer has disappeared from its original home, but it is bred in western, central and southern Europe and the western parts of the USSR.

Footprint

Roe Deer

Capreolus capreolus

The roe deer lives chiefly in forests, at both low and high altitudes, but in some regions it is being found more and more in fields. In western and central Europe the male weighs 15—20 kg, in eastern Europe up to 50 kg. The males are always larger than the females. The roe deer's body measures 95—135 cm and it stands 65—75 cm at the shoulder. Its summer coat is rusty red and its winter coat brownish grey.

Its antlers are less richly branched than those of the red deer. Three tines are very rare and four tines are almost unheard of. The antlers are shed at the end of October or in November and grow again in January and February.

Roe deer keep within the limits of their own preserve, the area of which is estimated at one square kilometre. As with all deer, their scent glands play an important part in their biology.

The rutting season lasts from the end of July to the middle of August. The male does not collect a group of females, but simply goes from one to another.

The gestation period is long (40 weeks). It is characterized by latent pregnancy, as the embryo does not start to develop until four months after the ovum has been fertilized. The young (usually twins) are born in May or June. The female suckles them into the winter, but they are already able to graze in their second month. Roe deer live chiefly on herbs and young shrub shoots.

The roe deer has a broken area of distribution. It inhabits Europe, where its most southerly point is Sicily, extends across Asia Minor to Mesopotamia and from northern Iraq to the mountains of central Asia and the Far East. It also lives in European Russia and the southern parts of the Urals.

Footprints on hard and soft surface

Elk

Alces alces

Deer
Cervidae

The elk, which weighs up to 560 kg and stands 235 cm at the shoulder, is the largest member of the deer family. It has a distinctive large, long, blunt snout with an overhanging upper lip and wide nostrils. It wears a mane on its short neck and has a leathery dewlap under its chin. The males can have huge palmated antlers with up to 30 tines, although elks often have only small, pronged antlers. The female is smaller than the male, weighs 270—380 kg and has no antlers. The elk has a very characteristic, sloping back. It is greyish brown to brownish black in colour, with light-coloured legs.

The elk is a forest-dweller. It inhabits northern Europe (Norway, Sweden and the north of the European part of the USSR), Siberia and North America.

During the past few dozen years there has been an enormous increase in the elk population and in the northern parts of eastern Europe it has started to penetrate further south.

Spreading forests broken by swamps and peat-bogs are the elk's natural habitat. It is more active in the evening and early morning, when it comes out to graze. Aquatic plants and young tree and shrub shoots are its favourite food. Rutting time usually starts at the end of August, but sometimes later, according to the latitude and the climate. When in rut, the males emit an obnoxious odour, but they have no strikingly characteristic call and they do not keep a harem like the red deer. The gestation period is 240—250 days and the 1—2 young are born in May or June. Young elks are all one colour, like young reindeer. Elks attain adulthood in their third year and have a life span of about 30 years. They like bathing, are excellent swimmers and can also dive.

Footprint

Reindeer

Rangifer tarandus

Unlike other deer, the female reindeer wears antlers, as well as the male. The antlers have a very distinctive form, as above the forehead their stem bends backwards and then curves forward again. The eye tine usually has a flattened tip. The female's antlers are generally thinner and have few branches. The reindeer is slighter than the red deer, the male weighing 120 to 150 kg and the female 105 — 120 kg; its shoulder height is about 100 cm. As distinct from other deer, it has wide hooves, to prevent it from sinking into the snow as it walks. Its summer coat is brownish grey, its winter coat whitish grey. Reindeer live in the circumpolar parts of the Old and the New World. Their herds mainly inhabit the vast treeless tundras and they are also to be found high up in the mountains. For about a century, the southern limit of the reindeer's area of distribution has been affected by man, whose activities have been steadily pushing it further north. In addition, wild reindeer have been largely replaced by the domesticated form employed by man. In Europe, there is still a small wild reindeer population (about 45,000) on Dovre-Rondane and on the Hardangervidda upland tundra in Norway. A number also live in Finland and the European part of the USSR.

Reindeer are gregarious animals living in troupes and herds. The rutting season is in the autumn. Rutting males are very restless and belligerent. They collect a harem of up to 20 females and drive rivals away. The 1 — 3 young are born in May or June. Reindeer living in the vast Arctic tundras migrate long distances twice a year. In Europe, where they are cramped for space, their movements are far more restricted than in Siberia or North America.

Footprint

European Wisent

Bison bonasus

The wisent is the largest European mammal. It measures 260—350 cm, stands 185—200 cm at the shoulder, its tail is 60—80 cm long and it weighs 800—1,000 kg. It was once found living wild in the forests of central and eastern Europe, but no longer.

Now it has disappeared forever from the forests of central and northern Europe. It survived the longest in the primaeval Bialowies Forest in Poland, where 1,898 specimens still lived in 1857. During the First World War this herd was decimated and by the end only 68 animals were left. Most of these were sold to different zoological gardens and menageries and the rest were hunted down. The last cow was shot in 1922. An international society to save the European wisent was then formed, a list of specimens living in captivity was drawn up and with suitable selection and breeding the number of wisents slowly started to increase again. Although at the time the society was founded there were only 30 specimens left in the world, by 1956 there were already 135 in Poland alone. In 1961 — likewise in Poland — 44 animals were set free as an experiment.

Wisents were also sent from Poland to other countries, on the assumption that their dispersion would save the basic stock from being destroyed by epidemics, etc.

In the natural state, wisents live in herds led by an old bull. Very old bulls live solitarily. They come out to graze mainly in the evening and early morning. During the rutting season (August and September), the bulls fight fiercely with each other. The gestation period is 9 months and the single calf is born in May or June. The wisent attains adulthood in its seventh year and has a life span of not more than 30 years.

Chamois

Rupicapra rupicapra

Together with the marmot and the snow vole, the chamois is a typical member of the mammalian fauna of certain mountain ranges in Europe and Asia Minor. It inhabits the Cantabrian Mountains, the Pyrenees, the Alps, the Abruzzi region, the Carpathians, parts of the Balkans, the Caucasus and the Pontus, Taurus and Anti Taurus Mountains.

The chamois' summer coat is reddish brown, with short hairs (about 3 cm) and a dark dorsal stripe. Its winter coat is almost black, with a white underside. Its legs and head are yellowish brown and its face is marked with pale yellow stripes. In the winter, long hairs, measuring up to 20 cm, grow at the side of the dark dorsal summer stripe. An adult male chamois weighs 35—50 kg, a female 30—40 kg. Both sexes have horns, curved more sharply in males. The kids already have horns in their first year, but they are only 4—5 cm long. In their second year about 9 cm is added to the length of the horns and in the third year 5 cm, the increase diminishing every year. Each year's growth leaves a mark on the horns, enabling us to tell the animal's age. According to these marks, the chamois probably has a life span of up to 25 years.

Chamois remain mainly on the mountain meadows above the tree line in the summer and come down to lower altitudes only in the winter. They can climb steep slopes and crags and can jump from rock to rock. Their best-developed senses are hearing and smell. They always roam in troupes and sometimes form large herds. Old males live solitarily. The female usually gives birth to only one young, after a 24—26 week pregnancy.

Chamois subsist mainly on short-stemmed mountain plants. In the winter they eat the leaves of trees and, if need be, will make do with dwarf pine needles.

Footprint

Mouflon

Ovis musimon

Hollow-horned Ruminants
Bovidae

The mouflon is the only wild European sheep. Originally it lived only on Sardinia and Corsica, but was introduced into central and western Europe, where it soon settled down in its new surroundings. Mouflons can be bred either in enclosed preserves or in hunting country.

Mouflons measure 100—125 cm, stand 65—75 cm at the shoulder and have a 10 cm tail. Old rams can weigh up to 50 kg, females about 6 kg less. The males have rugose horns, which curve downwards in a spiral and are roughly triangular in cross section. They start to grow during the animal's fourth month. The horns of an adult ram measure 70—80 cm, while the ewe has either short horns, or none at all. The mouflon's summer coat is rusty brown, with a dark brown back. Its underside and nose are white and it has a white perianal patch. Its winter coat is much darker. The rams have a long mane on their neck and chest and two light, squarish spots on their sides.

In their original home, mouflons inhabit mountains, rocky country and hillsides, but in their adoptive countries they live in large forests in both mountains and plains. They roam in herds led by an old ewe. Old rams are solitary, but attach themselves to a herd in the winter. In September, the rams look for groups of females. The rutting season lasts from October to the middle of December and the lambs are born five months later.

Mouflons live chiefly on herbs and grass, but also crop twigs, heather, bilberry plants, etc. In the autumn they collect acorns and berries growing on trees and bushes. In times of shortage they will even eat lichen and moss.

Footprint

Ibex

Capra ibex

Hollow-horned Ruminants
Bovidae

The ibex closely resembles the Persian wild goat. The latter's horns have a sharp ridge on their anterior surface, however, while the ibex's horns are flat and the grooves, in some forms, are much more pronounced. The ibex is a widely distributed species with several different geographical races, which were once regarded as separate species. The only places where the ibex is to be found in Europe are the Alps and the Iberian Peninsula. Further east, it occurs in the Caucasus, the mountains of central Asia, central Siberia, Kashmir, Afghanistan, Syria, Palestine and the Sudan.

The alpine ibex is a robust animal. The male, which is considerably larger than the female, is 130—160 cm long, stands 80—100 cm at the shoulder and weighs up to 110 kg. Its horns grow to a length of up to 1 m and are ringed with characteristic thick, knobbly ridges. The female's horns do not measure more than 30 cm. In the summer, the ibex wears a dark brownish grey or reddish brown coat; its winter coat is lighter.

The alpine ibex frequents altitudes between the upper limit of the tree belt and the permanent snow line. Rutting, which occurs in December and January, is accompanied by duels between the males. After a gestation period of 22 weeks, the female gives birth (usually in June) to a single young.

At one time, alpine ibexes lived throughout the Alps, but persecution reduced their population until, in the middle of the last century, only a few were left on the Gran Paradiso in the Carnic Alps in Italy. King Victor Emanuel II took this herd under his patronage, with the result that it increased in size, thereby making it possible to transfer some of the animals to other parts of the Alps.

Male's (left) and female's horns

Persian Wild Goat or **Pasang**

Hollow-horned Ruminants
Bovidae

Capra aegagrus

This goat has laterally flattened horns with a sharp ridge on their anterior surface. The horns, which curve backwards in a regular arc, grow to a length of up to 110 cm and have 10—12 rings, according to the animal's age. An adult male measures about 150 cm and stands 95 cm at the shoulder. The Persian wild goat's coat is reddish grey on the back and sandy yellow on the sides and has a sharply defined black dorsal stripe which narrows towards the tail. Between its neck and shoulders it has a broad black collar. The female also has horns, but they are thinner and shorter than those of the male.

The Persian wild goat inhabits various Mediterranean islands, Asia Minor, Iran, Transcaucasia and Afghanistan. As distinct from the ibex, it frequents the middle slopes of mountains rather than the higher parts. It forms small herds and groups, but the old males, except at rutting time, live solitarily. In the winter the goats collect in large herds. Their diet consists of herbs, leaves and young shrub and tree shoots. The rutting season lasts from November to December and the following May or June, i.e. after 21—23 weeks, the female gives birth to one or two young.

Measures taken for the protection of these animals have resulted in an increase in their numbers on the Mediterranean islands, making it possible to transplant some of them to other islands. The Persian wild goat can be crossed with domestic goats and since herds of domestic goats graze everywhere on the islands of the Mediterranean, it is sometimes hard to tell whether the goats on a given island are native Persian wild goats, or the descendants of domestic goats.

INDEX OF COMMON NAMES

INDEX OF LATIN NAMES